ABOUT THE AUTHOR

David Robbins has had well over three hundred books published under his own name and nine different pen name during a career that has spanned four decades. He is perhaps best known for his science fiction series *ENDWORLD* as well as his Mountain Man series *WILDERNESS*. His Horror books include *HELL-O-WEEN, PRANK NIGHT* and *SPOOK NIGHT*. Among his other notable novels are *HIT RADIO* and *HYPNOTWIST*.

BOOKS BY DAVID ROBBINS

The Endworld Universe

The ENDWORLD Series
The WILDERNESS series
The WHITE APACHE series
The BLOOD FEUD series
A GIRL, THE END OF THE WORLD AND EVERY-
THING

Horror:

PRANK NIGHT
SPOOK NIGHT
HELL-O-WEEN
THE WERELING
THE WRATH
SPECTRE

Novels:

HIT RADIO
BLOOD CULT

Westerns:

THUNDER VALLEY
RIDE TO VALOR
DIABLO
TOWN TAMERS
BADLANDERS
GUNS ON THE PRAIRIE

Other Series:

The ANGEL U series
DAVY CROCKETT

Nonfiction:

HEAVY TRAFFIC

THE BOY WHO WAS WORTHLESS

BY

DAVID ROBBINS

Published by Mad Hornet Publishing
Printed in the United States of America
ISBN: 978-1-950096-21-3

MAD HORNET
PUBLISHING

BEFORE HE WENT INSANE

His life was wonderful until the night his mom shot his dad.

He was born at 5:12 p.m. His mother, exhausted, held him in her arms in her hospital bed and said wearily, "Look at him, Stinky. He's so tiny."

His father, the youngest of three brothers and often called 'the runt of the family', smiled and said, "He won't always be, Stink."

Stink and Stinky were terms of endearment. It stemmed from the time they first made love on a hot summer's day and discovered sweat wasn't fragrant. It amused them so much that they had a plaster plate made that read: *Stink loves her Stinky and Stinky loves his Stink.* They hung it on their living room wall and enjoyed many a laugh at how some of their family and friends reacted.

Her name was Beatrice but no one ever called her that. It was Bea or Becky or Beck.

His name was Albert and he was always Al except for when his Stink called him Stinky.

Al's dad and mom didn't see the humor in the plate. They thought it was vulgar. In fact, they felt that their son shouldn't have married Becky. In their eyes she was from the wrong side of the tracks, as the saying went. She wasn't worthy of their son's affection.

Their estimate of her moral worth stemmed from what some might call the horror of her own father trying to molest her---not once but repeatedly.

Becky confided in the only person she could at the time, her father's sister, Evelyn, who in turn persuaded her husband---Tyson---to take the girl in on their farm in Pennsylvania Dutch Country.

It was the opinion of Becky's eventual father-and-mother in-law that where there was smoke, there must be fire. If the girl's father tried to molest her, she must have done something to encourage him.

Al and Becky met at a party on the Jersey Shore. She was small and shy and had virtually no experience with the real world beyond school and the farm and her few friends and her despicable bastard of a dad.

Her soon-to-be husband was fresh home from World War II. In her eyes he was a man of the world. At 5'5" and 120 pounds he was barely bigger than she was.

And so handsome.

Becky even liked his scars.

Al had two over his right eye. He didn't see them as scars. He saw them as badges of honor. Because of his size, when he was younger he was constantly picked on and belittled, even by his own brothers. It got so, Al bristled at the drop of a slight. As a boy he waded into much bigger boys and as a man into much bigger men, and the outcome be damned.

Al came to regard being tough as the best and foremost mark of what it meant to be a man. When World War II broke out he tried to enlist in the Army and the Navy but was refused because of flat feet.

Thanks to a friend and some finagling, he was able to join the United States Maritime Service. He served as a Merchant Marine Seaman aboard vessels in the Atlantic and the Pacific. He sailed the Mediterrean Sea and spent an entire day with buddies riding horses in Egypt.

He saw action on several fronts. The War Shipping Administration awarded him the Atlantic War Zone Bar, the Mediterranean Middle East War Zone Bar and the Pacific War Zone Bar.

After his discharge he returned to his town of birth to live with his parents and became a machinist. Soon after, he met Becky and proudly brought her to see his parents. They were friendly at first, even though Al's mother thought Becky wore too much makeup and especially too much lipstick and Al's father didn't like her tight sweaters and tops.

When they learned about the situation with her father, they discussed it, often, behind Al's back.

The wedding, fittingly, was small. Becky's aunt and husband came and Al's father and mother and brothers and several of Becky's friends and that was it. Becky's dad wanted to come but she told him no and Al, on the sly, told him that if he did, Al would take a crowbar to his skull.

Her dad stayed away.

The newlywed pair had little money and few possessions but they had each other and that was enough.

Al made a fair income and they were able to buy a *Masterbilt Canned Ham Camper Travel Trailer* that wasn't quite twenty feet long and not much more than half that wide. They lived in a trailer park and scrimped and saved to come up with the down payment on a house.

They were cramped and poor but they were in love and as happy as either had ever been.

Becky became pregnant.

They needed more money so Al took a second job as a garbageman. In subsequent years the proper title would be sanitation engineer but in the '50's no one suspected that emptying trash cans into the back of a dumpster truck required an engineering degree.

Al worked full-time at the manufacturing plant, from 8 to 5. On five nights a week he also worked from 4 a.m. until 7 a.m. at his second job. The long hours wore at him as did being away from Becky.

It wore at Becky, too. Al was her love and her life. Not having him there with her sapped her energy and her enthusiasm. Her pregnancy went well except for her morning sickness but being alone with only her belly for company was trying.

Stink and Stinky hung in there.

The momentous day came and their first child entered the world with apparent reluctance. Becky was in labor for hours. At last biology triumphed and there she was, holding him and saying, "Look at him, Stinky. He's so tiny."

They brought their new son home to their tin mansion, as Al jokingly called it. He continued to work two jobs.

The baby became Becky's whole life. She bought *Our Baby's Book* and kept a meticulous record of her newborn's development.

THE BOY WHO WAS WORTHLESS

At birth Butch weighed 6 pounds 15 ounces. By his first year he was up to 24 pounds.

Six days after his first birthday she wrote '*You said daddy for the first time.*' A month later he said 'mommy'.

She made a special note that '*You ate when you were hungry which was all the time.*'

At four months she made mention that '*you noticed your hands for 1st time.*' It made her grin that for the longest time he laid there and stared at them and moved his fingers as if figuring out what they were.

Eight months after he was born Becky wrote, '*1st respond to punishment. Corrected by voice and you cried*'. She added, '*You were chewing the ironing cord*'.

She made mention that he laughed for the first time at five months.

In the *Book* under *First Creeps* she wrote: *You creeped to your grand-dad from the living room to the kitchen.*' He was eight months. She added, '*We were all very proud of you.*'

A week after his first birthday Becky made this entry: '*You walked from the snack bar to the far end of the couch where daddy was sitting. Neither your daddy nor I could believe our eyes.*'

Nearly everything Becky did was baby-related. She fed him and nursed him and walked him at night and was always exhausted.

So was Al. Two jobs took their toll. Just when they were stretched thin emotionally, fate intervened. Al was given a promotion. Which meant more money. Enough that they could afford monthly house payments if the payments were low enough. They might not have money for much else but Becky was thrilled at the prospect of saying goodbye to the cramped trailer and having a real home of their very own.

But where to live?

They considered Norristown, where Al was born and raised. He loved it there but that was where his parents lived and he resented how they treated Becky. Although they tried to hide their feelings, Al knew his folks well enough to know that they weren't pleased about his choice in wives.

Al knew that Becky sensed it, too.

So, no Norristown.

They thought about somewhere near Valley Forge. Al loved the National Historical Park. Three thousand plus acres of rolling grassland and woods, old battlements and cabins, and cannons. As a boy he had roamed the Park with relish, inspired by the tale of George Washington struggling to win the American Revolution.

Another plus was that Valley Forge was close to where Al worked as a machinist. He wouldn't have to drive very far.

They looked at a few properties and were on the verge of buying a house that was barely within their means when the real estate agent mentioned some lots that were for sale at the very edge of Montgomery County. A dozen, all told, and the farmer who owned the land was willing to let the lots go dirt cheap.

In fact, Al and Becky could have a house built to their specifications and the combined cost would be less than the other properties they were considering.

Becky leaped at the prospect. Their very own home! Built as they wanted! Even better, the lots were on the slope of the highest hill in the entire county. The view was spectacular. On a clear day she swore she could see all the way to Philadelphia.

Living so far out didn't bother her. Their home would be part of a small neighborhood insulated from the rest of the world by thick woods on three sides. It would combine the best of surburban life with peace and quiet.

The hardest part for Becky was waiting for the house to be built.

Al continued to work two jobs. Becky protested. She pointed out that it was wearing him down and they could get by with his machinist's income alone.

That wasn't good enough for Al. He had a wife and a son and he would provide for them the best he was able. He was constantly racking his brain for a way to increase his income not just enough to live comfortably but enough to make them well off for the rest of their lives.

Al vividly remembered the Great Depression. His father, a machinist, too, was fortunate in that he kept his job. Al's mother, of course, didn't work. She was a homemaker. Women weren't supposed to get jobs. It was an insult to the man trying to provide for her.

Even so, even with Al's father working, those were hard, lean years where everyone in the family needed to account for every penny spent and didn't dare buy anything they didn't dearly need.

It left a lasting impression.

Al racked his brain and about two years after they

moved into their new home, inspiration struck.

In all that time Becky was happy beyond words. She was with a man she loved more than anything and had a son she adored and her very own home---as fine as she ever lived in. She was always smiling and humming, fit to burst with happiness.

Their son grew apace. He gurgled and cooed a lot. He also chewed everything he got his little hands on.

By the age of four he thinned and possessed a thick head of dark brown hair.

Al insisted that the boy have a crewcut---the same as his. As a result everyone took to calling the boy Butch.

Becky wasn't sure who started it---possibly Al himself---but she didn't mind. Butch was her darling son. Let them call him whatever they liked.

Butch was also a trifle weird.

For one thing, he was nearly always happy. He never cried, not even when he was teething, as most babies did.

Butch had a temper, again as most babies did, but his tamtrums were rare. And terrible to behold. He got so red in the face, Becky half thought he might explode.

At night, when many babies cried and wailed and kept their mothers from catching any sleep, Butch did none of that. He crawled around the edge of the crib, over and over and over, laughing and giggling. She would pick him up and try to soothe him into sleeping but when she put him down, he went to crawling and laughing again.

He did the same in the crib. She would find him moving from bar to bar, using them to stay on his feet as he laboriously went round and round the entire crib, laughing as he did.

When friends and acquaintances asked how her son was doing, she always mentioned he laughed a lot. Her nickname for him was My Happy Boy.

There was another thing Becky noticed.

Butch loved people. Not a little. A lot. Whenever anyone came to visit, he would toddle to them and hug their legs and smile and laugh. Once he learned to talk, he entertained guests by saying every word he'd learned and added unintellible gobblygook, beaming all the while.

Becky worried that maybe he was 'too' happy. She spoke to Al about it and Al told her she was being silly, that it was just Butch's nature. Butch had been the happiest of babies and now he was the happiest of boys and when he was older, God willing, he would be the happiest of grown men.

"Lord knows," Al commented as they sat at supper one evening, "the world could use more happy people."

In later years when asked if she could remember Butch being sad about anything before the night that changed their lives forever, she recalled only one instance.

It was when they were living in the trailer park.

One of Al's brothers gave them a pedigreed blond cocker spaniel.

Butch adored the dog. So much, they became inseparable. The puppy loved to lick Butch's face, and to Becky's great amusement and not a little revulsion, Butch would lick the dog's. They would sit there and lick and lick and she would laugh until her sides split and then she would separate them and clean the slime off Butch's face.

Often, Becky and Al would take Butch and watch the trains go by. Their trailer park was near railroad tracks.

Al would pump his arm and the engineer would sometimes wave and let off a blast of the whistle.

Butch always squealed in delight and clapped his hands.

One day Becky was busy cleaning.

Butch and Robby, the cocker spaniel, were outside near the front door, playing. She glanced out and saw them and returned to her work and after a few minutes was suddenly conscious that things were too quiet. She went to the screen door and didn't see them.

"Butch?"

Becky opened the screen door and poked her head out and looked right and left. They were nowhere in the small yard.

"Butch? Where are you?"

She draped the dust rag over her shoulder and went partway down the walk.

"Butch?"

The trailer park was quiet and the day still save for some crows cawing in the distance.

Becky glanced up and down the street. She heard a train whistle a ways off and turned toward the railroad tracks and her heart nearly leaped up her throat.

Robby was prancing toward the tracks and Butch was following, walking unsteadily but gamely to keep up.

Just then, around a bend to the south, the

locomotive appeared.

For a few anxious moments Becky was paralyzed with fright. Then her vocal chords unfroze and she screamed, "Butch!"

Her son went on waddling after the puppy.

Beckly flew. She had never been much of a runner but she ran now as never before. Her shoes smacked the asphalt and she was across the road and saw that the puppy was standing in the middle of the tracks.

Butch was trying to step over the near rail to join it.

The train came on, its speed unabated.

"*Butch*!"

Her son stopped and twisted to look back at her and smile.

The train was almost on them.

Out of the corner of her eye Becky saw the engineer poke his head out and see the boy and the dog. His shock was obvious. He frantically yanked to blast the whistle.

It all happened so terribly fast. Becky reached the tracks, fear filling every pore of her being. Butch was smiling and saying something.

The locomotive---a huge hurtling juggernaut---was almost on top of them.

Becky snatched Butch into her arms and spun, mashing his face into her chest, pressing so hard he squawked in alarm. Her last sight of the cocker spaniel was of it looking up at the onrushing engine. She heard a crunch and thought she heard a whimper and then the train was past and its brakes were screeching and the engineer yelled but his words were smothered by the screech.

Becky ran for their trailer. Butch pushed against her and cried out but she kept his face mashed to her bosom, practically smothering him. Only later did she realize why she had done it. To keep him from seeing. No one so young should see something so awful.

She made it to the trailer and ran inside and set him down and slammed the front door. Sagging against it, she gasped for breath, her whole body quaking and her heart thumping wildly.

Tears filled her eyes and she sagged to the floor. A small hand touched her cheek, giving her a start.

"Mommy?" Butch said.

Becky hugged him and sobbed and once again he tried to pull loose but only a couple of times and then he stopped resisting and let her cry and patted her arms and her shoulders.

She and Al never told Butch what happened to Robby. Al said that the dog ran off. Becky wanted to get another but Al said they should wait until they were in their new house.

Yes, Butch loved that dog. As much as he loved his pearl-handled revolvers.

Al was fond of movies. He took Becky to dozens. He especially liked Hopalong Cassidy, a favorite of his since he was little. So it was that Al bought Butch a Hopalong Cassidy outfit complete with a cowboy hat and a pair of plastic white-handled pistols.

Butch wanted to wear the outfit everywhere, even to bed. As for the guns, he would stand with the gunbelt around his small waist and jerk his pistols and spin them on his fingers and fan them and go *Bang! Bang! Bang!*

He couldn't get enough of doing that.

Al took a picture of Butch standing in front of their trailer holding his pistols and looking at them in great delight.

Becky didn't like guns but Westerns were hugely popular and Al assured her that playing with toy guns was perfectly normal and nothing bad would ever come of it.

Shortly after they moved into their new home, Al upset her by buying a rifle. A .22. Now that they lived in the country, Al said they needed the protection. Becky didn't see what they needed protecting from but she went along with it as she did with most everything Al wanted to do.

He was, after all, the love of her life.

Becky was happy. Content. Her father tried to guilt her into allowing him into their life and she coldly refused. When he died of a stroke while mowing his lawn she was secretly glad. Her memories of him during her younger years were pleasant enough. Until her mother died, anyway, and her father took to regarding her as a replacement.

Al made better money now thanks to periodic raises. Becky tried to talk him out of continuing to work his second job but he insisted it was necessary.

Al bought a motorcycle and took to wearing a brown leather jacket and he took to being gone one night a week.

Al's brother was to blame. Specifically, the second oldest, Micky. Becky never liked Micky much. He was too friendly toward her. Although he was married he frequented bars and owned a motorcyle of his own. Put simply, Micky liked to get drunk and have a high old time. Since he was closer to Al than the oldest brother, Joe---a devoted family man---Al liked to hang out with Micky more and do what Micky did.

Tuesday night became Men's Night Out. Why Tuesday, Becky didn't know. Micky would come over about six in the evening and the brothers would fire up their motorcyles and off they went. Frequently, Al didn't get home until midnight or later.

Becky didn't like it but she held her tongue. The last thing she wanted to be was a nagging wife. By now Butch was pushing seven so it wasn't a burden on her to look after him while Al was off doing whatever he was doing.

One time Al's parents came over for a Sunday afternoon visit and supper. As Becky and her mother-in-law were working in the kitchen, her mother-in-law mentioned that she had heard about Al and Micky gallavanting about one night a week.

Becky smiled and said it was good for Al to get out now and then and have a little fun.

Her mother-in-law turned and regarded her frostily. "A good wife is all the fun a husband should need."

Becky felt her cheeks grow warm with anger.

"A man won't let temptation get the better of him if his wife fulfills all his needs," her mother-in-law went on.

Becky bit her lip. She was tempted to give the old iceberg a piece of her mind but Al wouldn't like that and she was trying to stay on good terms with his family. "I guess I'll have to try harder."

"If you think you're capable, dear," her mother-in-law said.

With Al gone so much, what with two jobs and now Men's Night, Becky invested herself in her children.

Butch had acquired a little sister, Karen, who was three. He was adorable beyond words. Always smiling. Always a bundle of energy.

Sometimes he was also a pain in the neck.

Butch loved to chew things. Anything he got his hands on he tested with his mouth. Even gross things. When she caught him eating Robby II's food---Al got a German Shepherd for her as extra protection for when he was gone and kept it on a chain in the yard---Becky gave Butch a good talking to and explained that dog food was for dogs, not for people.

Butch went on eating it anyway. When she pressed him about why, he said that he was being a dog.

Much to Becky's annoyance, one day at the farm she caught him stuffing handfuls of grass into his mouth and chomping away and when she asked what possible reason he could have, he replied that he was being a cow.

Tablet paper. The rugs. Paper bags. Al's dirty socks. Her socks. Washrags. Couch cushions. Butch chewed and sucked on everything. The wonder of it was he didn't become sick.

It worried her, though. She mentioned it to Micky's and Joe's wives and they told her that it was perfectly normal for a child who was teething to chew on things.

Butch, however, was well past that phase.

Then came the day Becky caught him eating dirt.

She was carrying a basket of wash out the back door to hang on the clothesline and happened to glance to her left and stopped cold.

Her pride and joy was seated beside a hole the German Shepherd had dug and was scooping out dirt and putting the dirt in his mouth.

The dog was lying there watching him.

Becky was appalled. Setting down the basket, she went over and grabbed Butch by the wrist and yanked him to his feet.

"Mom?" the boy said, dirt dribbling over his lower lip. "What's the matter?"

Becky gave him a hard shake. "What in the world do you think you're doing?"

Butch pointed at the hole. "Being a worm."

It was the last straw.

Becky smacked him on the behind. Not once but several times. Not as hard as she could but close.

He didn't yelp or burst into tears or anything like that. He just looked up at her as if extremely puzzled and said, "What did I do?"

"Listen to me," Becky said angrily, giving him another rough shake. "Eating dirt can make you sick. It can give you diseases. I know. My mother warned me about it."

"It tastes good," Butch said.

"It's *dirt*," Becky practically shrieked. "People don't eat dirt! People eat normal food! You're never to do this again, do you hear me?"

"Let go of me," Butch said, and tried to pull free.

"Do you hear me, young man?" Becky said.

"Let go," Butch said, tugging harder. "You're being

mean."

"I'll give you mean if I ever catch you eating anything you shouldn't ever again. From now on you eat what we eat and nothing else."

"Let go!" Butch threw his whole body back but she held on and he clawed at her wrist with his other hand.

"Don't you dare!" Becky said, and gave him several more swats on his bottom. Letting go, she put her hand against his back and pushed him toward the door. "In you go, buster! You're confined to your room until I say otherwise."

When Al came home from work Becky told him about the incident and showed the scratch marks on her wrist from where Butch clawed her.

Al's face grew hard. "We can't let that go unpunished, hon."

"I confined him to his room."

"That's not enough." Al undid his belt buckle and began to remove his belt.

"What are you doing?"

"He has to learn to never lay a hand on us." Al grasped the ends of the belt and headed into the hall to the childrens' bedroom.

Karen was in the living room playing with a doll. She didn't look up as they went by.

Al opened the bedroom door and Becky followed him in.

The room contained a bunkbed and a toy chest and a small table and chair.

Butch was on the top bunk. "Hi dad."

"Come down here," Al said.

Butch climbed down the ladder and looked

expectantly up at his father.

"You hurt your mother."

"I did not," Butch said in surprise.

"Show him your wrist," Al said to Becky.

She reluctantly did.

"You scratched her," Al said. "You raised your hand to her. It is something you must never do. To either of us. We are your parents. Do you understand?"

"I didn't mean to," Butch said.

"What you meant and what you did are two different things." Al motioned with the belt. "Turn around and face the wall."

"What are you going to do?" Butch said.

"Turn around."

Butch glanced at Becky---and did as he was told. "I didn't mean to," he said again.

"A man has to own up to his mistakes," Al said.

Becky almost broke in with 'He's just a boy!' but she held her tongue.

Al raised the belt and paused. "I'm sorry I have to do this son. My dad did it to me more times than I can remember. For my own good. Do you understand?"

Butch didn't say anything.

Al swung.

At the sharp crack of the belt against Butch's backside, Becky flinched.

Al swung again and again and again. Six. Seven. Eight times. Finally he stopped and stared at Butch as if perplexed.

Not once did their son cry out. Not once did he seek to shift away from the blows. At each contact he swayed a little but that was all. He just stood there, his back to them.

"Son?" Al said.

Butch turned. He was red in the face but hadn't broken out in tears. He seemed angry more than anything. "Dad?"

"Didn't that hurt?"

"It hurt a lot."

"Why aren't you crying?"

"You told me not to, remember?"

"What?" Becky said.

Al lowered his belt and commenced to put it back on. "Did you learn your lesson?"

"I learned a lot," Butch said.

"Good."

Al gestured and after Becky preceded him out, he said, "You're to stay in your room until I say different."

Butch didn't respond.

Becky waited until they reached the kitchen to say, "What was that about you telling him not to cry?"

Al opened the refrigerator and took out a bottle of milk. "Oh that. Well, you know how he likes to watch me take my baths?"

Becky nodded. It started when Butch was little. He refused to bathe himself once he was old enough, so Al, who took three baths a week, made the boy sit in the bathroom and watch him take one. The idea being that Butch would realize there was nothing to it, and if his dad took them, he should too.

It became their custom for Butch to sit on the toilet seat when Al was in the tub and the two would talk.

"I was washing my hair and the shampoo dripped into my eyes," Al explained as he filled a glass. "Butch asked me if it stung. He told me that sometimes when you wash him the shampoo gets into his eyes and stings like the dickens."

"So?" Becky said when Al stopped.

"I told him it did but I didn't let it bother me. That men don't let things like that get to them."

"The crying part?"

Al took a swallow and smacked his lips. "This was delivered this morning, wasn't it?"

"The crying?" Becky prompted.

"Oh. He mentioned seeing you cry a couple of times. Like when the cocker spaniel died. He didn't, and he wondered if he should have. If men ever cry, as he put it."

"What did you tell him?"

Al drained half the glass and smacked his lips once more." I learned at an early age that men need to be tough. All those guys who picked on me because I'm so short? The ones who thought they could beat me up for the fun of it? They learned different." Al finished the milk. "I told Butch that no matter what, a man must be tough inside as well as out. That real men don't ever cry."

"Oh Al," Becky said.

"What? You want him to grow up to be a bawl-baby? To cry like a girl at every little thing?"

"That's not fair," Becky said. "I don't cry at every little thing."

"You're special."

"Nor do most women," Becky insisted.

"Anyway, that's what I told him," Al said.

"So he took the belting you gave him and didn't

cry," Becky marveled.

"Didn't let out a peep," Al said proudly.

Something was different about Butch after that. Becky couldn't put her finger on exactly what. It wasn't that he was cold or aloof or anything but it was there. Something subtle.

Their life went on.

A third child, another boy, joined their growing family. Mark, they named him.

Butch was still a dynamo, still smiled and laughed a lot. His favorite thing was to play with his plastic cowboys and Indians and army men---Al bought him a *Fort Dearborn* and a *Roy Rogers Ranch* set. He was extra fond of his *Payton Foreign Legion* and *Robin Hood* figures. The latter stemmed from his intense interest in the *The Adventures of Robin Hood* TV show. It was his favorite next to *Ramar Of The Jungle*.

Becky would listen in when he played and be delightfully surprised as how he changed his voice for the different characters and animals and how he would concoct little shows in themselves.

In school he did so-so.

Al and her sat him down in the kitchen one day and asked why he wasn't doing better given that they both felt he was uncommonly bright.

Butch replied that school didn't interest him much. Most of the time he shut the teachers out and doodled tiny stick cowboys and army men in his tablet.

Becky wondered if it had something to do with his first day of school---he had thrown a fit. He refused to go. He said it wasn't right that school would take him away from them. She explained that all boys and girls his age were required to go to school whether they wanted to or not.

"Who says we have to?" Butch demanded.

"It's the law," Becky said. "I told you about laws before. How you can't do bad things or you find yourself behind bars."

"Where do laws comes from?"

Becky shrugged. "It's probably one the legislature passed."

"The what?"

"Politicians."

"What are they?"

"They tell us how to live."

Butch appeared shocked. "Someone can do that?"

Becky gave a brief summary of how citizens elected people to serve in the House and Senate and how they passed laws for the good of everybody.

"I don't like going to school," Butch said sullenly. He didn't like the idea of other people telling him how he should live. And there was another reason. The girl he sat next to at the very back of the class would now and then wet herself and not say anything to the teacher. The stink of her pee was awful.

"You don't like learning?"

"I learn from you and dad."

"We don't know all there is to know. Plus there are all the other kids your age," Becky said. "You can make friends."

"Some of them are mean. I don't like mean."

"No one does, son. But you don't have any choice. You can't break the law."

"I don't like laws either."

"That's just silly." Becky decided to change the subject by saying, "The cartoons will be on soon."

Next to his toys, Butch enjoyed TV most. Becky had mildly objected when Al suggested they buy one. It was a big expense.

The TV itself turned out to be an attractive box-affair with an oval screen in the middle. It wasn't very big. They needed to huddle close for all of them to watch at the same time.

The shows were in black and white.

Becky remembered when they first brought it home. Butch learned that a *Superman* show was aired. He became so excited. He asked when it was and she told him the next day at five.

That night, Al and her were in bed sound asleep when she was awakened by a peculiar hum. It took her a few seconds to realize what was making it. Bewildered, she glanced at the clock. It was 4:55 a.m.

Donning her robe, Becky sleepily trudged out into the living room and there was Butch, cross-legged on the floor in front of the TV, his elbows on his knees, his chin in his hands, staring fixedly at the Indian Head Test Pattern.

Programs started at six in the morning and ran until midnight, at which point the national anthem was played and the test pattern symbol came on.

"What are you doing, son?" Becky asked.

"Waiting for Superman," Butch informed her.

Going over, Becky crouched and draped an arm around his shoulders. "Oh, son, son," she said tenderly. "I'm so sorry. The show doesn't come on until five in the afternoon."

Al came down the hall, scratching himself and yawning. "What in blue blazes is going on?"

Becky explained and they shared a good laugh.

"I didn't want to miss it," Butch said.

Other shows he liked were *Flash Gordon*, *Commando Cody*, and *Popeye*.

In the evenings the whole family watched things like *Ed Sullivan* or the *George Burns and Gracie Allen Show* or *Disneyland*. Becky's favorites were *I Love Lucy*, *Our Miss Brooks* and *Lawrence Welk*. Al couldn't get enough of *Life of Riley* and *The Honeymooners*.

Al also couldn't get enough of the boxing and wrestling shows and had Butch watch with him. They never missed *Friday Night Fights*. Butch's questions about boxing led Al to teach him the basics.

Becky would watch 'her men' jabbing and feinting and have a good grin.

She didn't grin much on Saturday afternoons. That was when the brothers came to visit. Micky always, Joe not so often. They would set up their amps and play music, Al on bass, Micky on the guitar. They formed a band, and now Al was sometimes gone on Friday or Saturday night to play at taverns or wherever.

Al's favorite music was Country. His favorite singer was Hank Williams. His favorite song was *Your Cheatin' Heart*.

Al also loved the outdoors and took Butch for a lot of walks in the surrounding woods. One time Butch came back excited because they came across a two-headed snake. Another time they stumbled on a mother rabbit with newborn baby rabbits. They actually saw the mother give birth.

Becky braced for a slew of questions about how human babies came into the world but Butch showed no curiosity whatsoever, which was unusual. So unusual, she mentioned it to Al.

He chuckled and said, "He asked me about it and I explained how it is with people."

"You told him about the birds and the bees? At his age?"

Just then Butch came in from outside and Al said, "Son. Your mother wants to know if you know where babies come from."

Butch nodded. "I know it all, mom."

"Oh Lord," Becky breathed.

"Where do babies come from, son?" Al said.

"A stork brings them."

Becky almost snorted out loud.

"Tell her the rest," Al said.

"They're special storks," Butch said. "They're trained to be nice to babies like we trains dogs to be nice to people and then they carry the babies like piegons carry messages."

"You don't say," Becky said with a straight face, and couldn't resist asking, "But where do the storks find the babies they bring?"

"A baby factory," Butch said. "Like where dad works only instead of trunks for storing stuff and the other things dad makes, they make babies. They do it so ladies don't have to go through what the mommy rabbit went through."

Butch went on down the hall.

"I can't believe he bought that," Becky said.

"It's all those cartoons," Al said.

Three children meant the kids' room was becoming crowded, what with the bunk bed for Butch and Karen and a crib for Mark.

By this time most of the lots along the lane had been sold and houses built on both sides of theirs and across the street. Two of Becky's neighbors were young mothers, like herself. They enjoyed getting together to swap stories about the pleasures and travails of child raising.

She also met their husbands.

WHEN HE WENT INSANE

Butch loved life. There was so much to do, so much to the world around him to explore, so many new sights and sounds and people.

He liked people. He liked his uncles and their wives and his cousins. He liked his grandparents although neither were as friendly and warm toward him as others.

He liked things that made him feel good. Playing with his toys. Ice cream and candy.

He liked comics. When he was five his father bought him **Dell** *Tarzan* #65 which showed Tarzan in a cave smiling at little N'kima while outside a storm raged. His father helped him read it and when they got to the part where the baby elephant was caught in a rushing river, he was afraid for the baby's life. He loved how Tarzan rescued it.

Ever after, the Dell and later Gold Key *Tarzan* comics were his favorites of all.

He loved going on 'nature walks', as his dad called them, and learning about all the animals and plants and whatnot. It never occurred to him that some of the creatures in the wild might be dangerous until his father and Uncle Micky brought home a monster turtle.

It happened that he was in the kitchen when his

mother called for him to the back door to see what his father had brought home. Thinking it might be a new toy---and how he loved toys---he went to where his mother stood holding the screen door open.

At the bottom of the steps were his dad and uncle, his dad holding a long pole with a metal hook at the end.

Near them on the grass was the biggest turtle Butch ever saw.

He was familiar with box turtles. They were common in the woods. He and his dad came across them often and Butch delighted in seeing them retract into their shells when he went to touch them. His dad showed him that when they retracted, he could get them to stick their heads out again by rubbing their bellies.

Butch had seen a couple of painted turtles, too. They lived in the creek.

None compared to this.

"What is it?" he marveled.

"A snapping turtle," his father said.

"Your dad caught it," Uncle Micky said.

His father wagged the pole and grinned. "Put up a fight, too. Watch. I'll show you something." He glanced at Butch's mom. "Get a slice of bologna."

Butch was mesmerized. The turtle was so huge, its head so thick. "Can I touch it?" he asked, thinking it would retract and he could rub its belly like he did with box turtles.

"Not unless you want to lose some of your fingers," his dad warned him.

His mother opened the refrigerator and took out a

pack of bologna and removed a slice. She brought it to Butch. "Give this to your father."

Butch was only on the second step when his father told him to stop.

"Don't get too close."

His dad took the bologna. "This is why you never touch a snapper."

His father stuck the bologna onto the hook at the end of the pole and then stepped back and extended the slice toward the turtle.

Suddenly the snapper's head seemed to shoot out and its mouth opened wider than Butch would have believed possible and it grabbed the slice between its jaws.

"See that?" his father said. "See how dangerous it is?"

"Don't ever go near a snapper, son," his mother stressed.

"What are you going to do with it, dad?" Butch wanted to know.

"Kill it and cut it up so your mother can make snapping turtle soup."

"Eat a turtle?"

"You eat beef which comes from cows and you eat chicken and fish," his father said. "This is no different. You'll love it. I promise you."

Butch did. The soup was delicious. He especially liked it with lots of butter. But then he liked butter a lot anyway. When his parents weren't watching he would sometimes go to the butter dish and run a finger along the top of the butter and then lick his finger in delight. He did the same with sugar. His mom was always saying not to, but butter and sugar just tasted so wonderful, he couldn't resist.

Butch liked the weekend music sessions his dad took part in. His father's band would play and he would dance and sing and the mothers would clap and tell him what a darling boy he was.

One morning when he was seven he came down to breakfast.

His father had gone out with Uncle Micky the night before to a movie. He mentioned how Butch would like the movie a lot but he couldn't watch it until he was older because it was scary.

"What's it about?" Butch asked, and spooned more *Frosted Flakes* into his mouth.

"A creature from another planet."

"We have those?"

His father and mother laughed and his father went on. "No. It's a movie. Movies aren't real. This one is called *The Thing From Another World*. The creature comes here in a flying saucer and wants to take over the world. It lives on human blood...."

"Al," his mother said.

Butch stopped chomping. "Gosh. What kind of thing is it?"

"Sort of a carrot."

"A what?" Butch said, not sure he had heard right.

"An intelligent carrot is how they describe it."

"A carrot like in our garden?"

His father nodded.

Butch rocked with laughter. He tried to swallow the rest of the cereal and gagged and coughed until it went down. "A carrot?" he said, and laughed louder.

His father and mother looked at each other.

"What's so funny?" his dad.

"You made that up," Butch declared.

"I did not. It's what the movie is about."

"A carrot from another world? And it drinks our blood?" Butch laughed some more.

"I would never lie to you, son," his father said.

"You're teasing me."

"You don't believe me?"

Butch shook his head and chuckled.

"Oh, son," his mother said.

His father frowned and got up and went out the back door. "I have a lawn to mow."

"You hurt his feelings," Butch's mother said.

Butch still refused to believe the movie was real. The idea was too silly. A carrot....from outer space?

He would have occasion to remember their exchange later, and to feel great guilt over calling his dad a liar.

Another incident he would feel guilty about occurred when his father took him to a veteran's meeting. There was food and prizes were given away. Everyone who entered the hall was given a ticket and after the meal, a man stood at a microphone and called out numbers and whoever had a ticket with one of the numbers won a prize.

Butch was excited. He had seen the prizes on a table and some of them were toys. He particularly wanted a 30-piece *Rel Davy Crockett* set that included soldiers and a wagon and horses and a cannon.

Everyone was having a grand time. The numbers were called and the winners would go up to receive their prizes and those in the chairs applauded.

Each number, Butch looked expectantly at his father, who was holding the ticket, and always shook his head.

Only one number was left, for the *Rel* set. It was called and Butch's father shook his head and Butch let out a scream and lost control. He screamed and wailed and stomped his feet and made such a spectacle that his dad turned red in the face and all the people were staring.

Butch went on and on, his dad trying to calm him, when to Butch's amazement and delight, the elderly man who had won the set came over and gave it to his dad, saying that a boy Butch's age better deserved such a prize.

His father didn't seem happy about it but he accepted the blister pack the set came in and gave it to Butch.

Butch beamed and clasped it close and shed more tears, this time tears of happiness. He noticed that his father didn't appear pleased but he didn't care. He had the set! Nothing else mattered.

When they were in the jeep heading home his father said, "Do you have any idea what you did back there?"

"I got the prize," Butch said happily.

"Where did your mother and I go wrong?" his father said sadly.

When they got home his father and mother went off in a corner and talked in low tones and kept glancing at Butch as he played with the soldiers. He didn't pay them much mind. He was just glad his dad didn't take a belt to him.

Ever since that first time, his dad had taken to belting him whenever his dad thought he misbehaved. Like when he was caught eating sugar. Or when he rummaged through their dresser drawers and made a mess. Or if he dared raise his voice to either of them.

That changed the day the lamp broke.

He was rushing in from outside and when he pushed on the front door it wouldn't open all the way. Something was behind it, blocking it. He pushed harder and heard a loud crash and then the door was wide and he saw a busted lamp on the floor and the end table it had been on near the back of the door.

His mother was vacuuming but the sound stopped and she came hurrying over. "Butch! What have you done!"

"I didn't know the table was there."

"I moved it to vacuum," his mother said, kneeling to gather the bits and pieces of lamp.

Footsteps sounded on the stairs to the cellar and his father appeared. "What was that crash? Butch broke that?"

"I didn't mean to," Butch said.

His father unbuckled his belt. "You always have an excuse, don't you?"

"Al, it was an accident," his mother said. "I had slid the end table over against the door."

"He needs to learn to be more careful." His father pulled the belt free and looped it. "We let him get away with entirely too much."

"Do we really?" his mother said.

His father pointed at a spot on the floor. "Stand

over here, son."

"I don't want to," Butch said. To his way of thinking this was wrong. Terribly wrong. He'd broken the lamp by mistake. Not on purpose.

"Do as I say, young man," his father said sternly.

Butch was slow to comply. To be belted for sneaking sweets was one thing. This was something else entirely. He stood with his back to his dad, his whole body on fire with anger. "It isn't right."

"We're your parents," his father said. "We decide what's right and what isn't."

"But dad....," Butch got out.

The belt struck his bottom hard enough to cause him to jerk a step forward.

"Stand still and take your medicine."

The belt struck again and Butch grit his teeth and clenched his fists, more furious than ever. "This isn't right!"

"We decide what's right and what's wrong, not you," his father said.

The blows became harder.

"Why isn't he crying?" his mother said. "I would be bawling my brains out."

"He's not crying to spite us," his father said.

This was the last straw. Butch had taken it to heart when his dad told him that men must be strong, that men must never cry.

He had wanted to that time his dad picked him up and chucked him into the deep end of a swimming pool. They were at a country club as part of a special day arranged for the factory's workers. His mom had taken his hand and led him to the pool's edge and told him to jump.

Butch shook his head.

"What's holding things up?" his father asked.

"He doesn't know how to swim," his mother said. "Remember?"

"We'll fix that right quick," his father said, and scooping Butch up, threw him into the pool.

Butch heard his mother cry out as he went under. The water was cold and clammy and stung his eyes. He felt himself sinking, going down deeper and deeper. Vaguely, above him, he could see his mother crouched at the edge, a hand to her throat. He needed air and swallowed and water gushed into his mouth and nose. Without thinking, he kicked and thrashed and swung his arms and the next thing he knew, he was rising toward the surface. He broke clear and gasped and gulped and his mother grabbed him and hauled him out. He lay spewing water and feeling half sick.

His father was laughing like crazy.

"Al!" his mother said.

"Did you see?" his father said. "He learned real quick!"

Butch felt his father's hands and he was lifted to his feet, still choking, and patted hard on the back a couple of times.

"I'm proud of you, son," his father said. "You did fine?"

"I did?" Butch got out between gasps.

"Yes. You learned to swim first time out. Now you need never be afraid of water." His father patted him a couple more times. "You were strong. You were a man."

Butch decided to be a man now. This beating was

wrong. He wasn't to blame. His fury overcoming him, he pried at his own belt and started to take it off.

"What is he doing?" his mother said.

His father paused with his belt raised on high. "What *are* you doing?" he demanded.

By then Butch had his belt off and turned. His was much smaller and much thinner. "This isn't right. I won't let you hit me anymore."

His father's face hardened. "Is that so?"

Butch bobbed his chin.

"For your information," his father said, "you don't decide when and how you'll be punished. We do."

"I mean it," Butch warned.

"So do we," his father said, and swung.

The belt caught Butch across the left shoulder. He swung his own belt, hitting his dad across the legs. The next moment they were both swinging as fast and as hard as they could. Butch felt pain after pain, sting after sting, but he didn't care. He was hit on the head and neck and shoulders and chest, but he didn't care. He swung as strong as he could and as high as he could and they turned back and forth and this way and that and somehow came to the hallway to the back rooms. He was aware of his mother yelling for them to stop but he wasn't going to unless his father did.

Out of nowhere his mother was there. Only she wasn't trying to stop it. She had her own belt and commenced swinging at Butch too, shouting something about him needing to behave.

It made Butch madder. Both his parents were in the wrong and he was in the right and he wouldn't quit no matter what. He kept swinging, swinging, not really sure where he was swinging or even who he was swinging at.

The three of them were moving wildly round and round down the hall. They came to the bedroom and Butch backpedaled to gain space.

Unexpectedly, his father stopped and lowered his belt and looked at Butch as if in amazement. Equally unexpected, he threw back his head and started to laugh. "Did you see him?" he got out between bursts. "Did you see our boy stand up to us?"

Suddenly Butch began laughing, too. The whole thing struck him as hugely funny. The three of them, belting away.

His mother stared at his father and then at him and she shook her head and then she commenced to laugh, too.

Before Butch knew it, all three of them were on the floor, laughing so hard they couldn't stand.

From that day on, his father never struck him again. In fact, that evening after supper his father set him down and said he was sorry about the beating, that he had given it much thought and Butch was right and shouldn't have been blamed for breaking the lamp.

Butch felt extra close to his father after that.

Their life went on.

In the Fall of his eighth year Butch's father took him to see go-cart races. A friend of his dad's had entered a cart.

His mother stayed home.

The races were being held in the parking lot of a factory up toward Collegeville. Boys of all ages could enter and race based on their age group. Younger boys against younger boys. Older boys against older boys.

The day was sunny and bright and Butch was having a grand time. The go-carts were fast and noisy and some of them were painted vivid colors.

He clapped and squealed in delight at how fast the carts went and the tremendous din.

For over two hours the very sky resounded with roars and cheers.

Then the races ended and people began to drift away. Butch thought they would leave too but his father surprised him by taking his hand and leading him to where a man and a boy older than Butch were bent over a go-cart. The man was his dad's friend.

They talked, and the man said that his son had come in third in a field of nine and he was proud of him.

Butch had seen the race and told the boy he drove really well.

"How come you didn't enter?" the boy asked.

Butch's father answered that they didn't have a cart but maybe someday Butch would.

"So he's never driven one?" his father's friend said. "Would he like to?"

Butch's dad was delighted by the idea. "What do you say, son? Want to give it a try?"

Butch stared at the go-cart. It was bright red with large tires. He wasn't sure if he wanted to or not. For some reason he thought about the swimming pool.

"No one is using the track," the friend said. "He can take a lap for the fun of it."

"I learned when I was his age," Butch's dad said.

Before Butch quite knew what was happening, his

dad lifted him and placed him in the go-cart. The friend squatted and put both of Butch's hands on the steering wheel and showed him how to turn it. He said other things but Butch didn't hear him. His whole body seemed to be thumping with the beat of his heart. Then he could hear again and his father was bent over him.

"Off you go."

"How do I make it go?" Butch said.

The friend pointed at a small metal petal under Butch's right foot. "That's the gas, remember? Press on that and you can go as fast as you want."

"Easy does it," his father said.

The friend gave the cart a pat and they stepped back.

Butch pushed on the pedal and the go-cart moved. Slowly at first.

"Faster!" someone shouted.

Butch pressed harder and the go-cart picked up speed. The motor growled fit to burst his eardrums and the wind was in his face and he laughed at the sheer thrill of it. He came to a bend and turned the wheel as he had been told and whipped around into a long straight stretch that appeared to go on forever. He pressed harder still on the pedal and the go-cart was flying. He glanced to his left across the track and saw his father and the friend and a few other people jumping up and down and waving their arms and yelling. He thought they were cheering him on. He went faster.

Another turn appeared and it occurred to him that maybe he should slow down a little. But how? He didn't remember anyone telling him. He figured if he took his foot off the pedal that maybe that was how you stopped so he did and the go-cart slowed but it was still going fast as anything when he reached the curve.

From then on everything happened so fast.

Butch turned the steering wheel as quickly as he could but the go-cart slewed and weaved and shot off the track across a tract of grass.

People were screaming.

Butch saw trees, one in particular, a big one he was heading straight for and he stomped his feet against the floor to brace himself and the go-cart slowed some more but it was much too little and much too late.

The tree filled his vision and there was a crash that might be the end of the world and he thought his head smashed into the steering wheel and then there was nothing.

Butch came awake.

Just-like-that he was aware of sounds and pain---so much pain---and he lay still, his eyes closed, and tried to make sense of things.

Someone close by was crying. He recognized who. It was his mother.

He heard his father say, "There, there. Stop this. He'll be all right."

"You don't know that!" his mother said, and weeped louder.

"He hasn't bled much. You did a good job with the bandage."

"We need to take him to the hospital!"

"Calm down. He hit his head, is all. It knocked him out but he'll be fine."

"He broke his nose!"

"No, I don't think it's broken. It's just sort of dented. We'll give him a while. An hour, say. If he hasn't come around then, yes, we'll take him to the hospital."

"Just because we don't have the money....."

"Becky, stop. This is getting us nowhere."

Butch heard her sniffle. He tried to say something, to let them know he was all right, but his mouth was too dry and his throat wouldn't work. He cracked his eyes open and couldn't make sense of what he saw. There was a large white shape on his face, over his nose. It rose to a point.

He tried to lick his lips but couldn't.

Forcing himself, he turned his head.

His mother and father were on the couch, which meant he must be on the party sofa. His mother was bent over, crying, and his father had an arm around her and was trying to comfort her.

Butch forced his mouth to move. "Mom? Dad?" he croaked.

Both leaped up and rushed over. His mother tried to cradle him and was crying and smiling at the same time and kissing his head and his cheeks.

His father placed a hand on his shoulder. "How are you feeling, son?"

"Okay," Butch said even though he wasn't.

"How bad are you hurting?"

"Not much," Butch said. Men didn't let pain get to them and he very much wanted to be a man in his father's eyes.

"You could have been killed," his mother said. "It was careless of your father to let you ride that go-cart."

"It was fun until the end," Butch said.

"You must be in a lot of pain," his mother said. "I have aspirin. I'll fetch you some." She went to rise. "Most boys would be crying over this."

"Men don't cry, mom," Butch said.

His father smiled and patted him. "That's my boy."

It took a couple of weeks for Butch to recover to where he could run and play like before. After the bandage was removed and he could touch his nose again, he found out his father was right. His nose had a dent in it right where it joined his forehead. He could press there and feel a groove in the bone.

Once again life went on. His sister was growing and his brother wasn't walking yet.

Butch could never quite remember how soon after the go-cart incident that he first heard his parents argue. It was late at night. He was asleep in the top bunk when their voices woke him. He lay listening and heard tones he never heard before. Harsh tones. As if they were angry. After a while their voices stopped and he went back to sleep.

There were more times. Always on nights when his father was off with his uncle or the band.

Came a night when harsh voices woke Butch out of another sound slumber. He couldn't quite make out what they were saying but it was obvious his father was extremely upset.

He glanced at the crib where his baby brother was sound asleep and bent over the side of his bunk to see his sister had not woken up, either.

A sharp sound, as of something hitting a wall or maybe smacking a table, startled him into sitting up.

Concerned, he descended the ladder.

Their voices were so loud, it was a wonder his sister and brother could sleep through it.

Butch moved to the bedroom door. It was closed. Usually it was kept open. He thought about going out but hesitated. His parents might not want him to interrupt. Instead, he lay on his side on the floor facing the door with his ear to the crack between the bottom of the door and the floor.

"....doing over there?" his father was saying.

"Just visiting," his mother said angrily.

"This late? You expect me to believe that?"

"Keep your voice down. You'll wake the kids."

"What if I do?" his father said, and he was angry, too. "This isn't the first time. I can't believe you would do this to me."

"You're a fine one to talk. Out all hours at bars and whatnot. Leaving me alone."

"Is that what this is about? Is that why you're giving yourself to ---."

Butch heard the name of a neighbor and for some reason felt a fierce hatred of the man.

"I keep telling you," his mother said. "I wasn't visiting him. I was visiting -----." She mentioned the man's wife.

"You expect me to believe that?"

"Keep it down! I don't want the kids to hear!"

Their voices moved farther away and became a jumble of sounds. Butch caught words here and there but the main thing was that they were being mean to each other. More than mean. Vicious. They were saying bad words and his dad was in a rage and his mother was madder than he ever heard her.

Butch was scared. He was afraid they would hurt each other. He didn't know what to do. He started to cry, he was so upset. He cried, and then he remembered a talk he had with his mom once about how when people were in trouble with no one else to turn to, they should turn to God for help.

In Sunday School he had learned all about God and the Bible. How God loved everyone and was there for them in times of need.

Butch prayed. His face wet with tears, he asked God to stop his mother and father from fighting and for them to be nice to each other. He prayed and he prayed as their voices went on and on and his eyes grew heavy with the need for sleep but he prayed more and he was still praying when he fell asleep.

Butch woke slowly.

He was flat on his back on something soft and a blanket was pulled to his chin. He imagined he was in his bunk but whatever he was lying on was a lot softer. He felt strange and itchy all over.

Near him someone coughed.

Butch opened his eyes to find Dr. Watson in a chair, scribbling notes. He looked down at himself and realized he was in his parents' bed. Why on earth he would be there was beyond him. The same with Dr. Watson. What was their doctor doing in their very house? The only time he saw Dr. Watson was when he was sick and his mom took him to the doctor's office in Norristown.

The itching grew worse.

Butch wanted very much to scratch his neck and tried to raise an arm but he was too weak. His movement attracted the doctor's attention.

"You're awake, David!" the doctor said as if surprised.

"Butch," Butch said. "Everyone calls me Butch." Again he tried to stir but couldn't.

"Lie still," Dr. Watson said, coming over to sit on the edge of the bed. "You're very ill."

Butch had always liked him. Watson was kind and had a friendly smile. "I'm sick? What from?"

Dr. Watson hesitated. "A form of hives. Your mother says you're allergic to strawberries and you had strawberry ice cream before you went to bed. I put Calamine lotion on so they won't itch quite as much."

Butch didn't remember eating any ice cream but if his mother said he did, then it must be so. Truth was, his head didn't feel right. He struggled for each thought. "What does allergic mean?"

"Some people can eat certain things that other people can't. You ate the strawberry ice cream and it gave you the hives."

There was that word again. "The what?" Butch said.

Dr. Watson raised Butch's left arm and eased back the sleeve to his pajama top. "See?"

Butch did. His skin was peppered with pink splotches about the size of a quarter. Some were raised a bit as if they were trying to grow. "Is that what these are?"

"I think so, yes."

Butch had a more important question. "Where are

my mom and dad?"

Dr. Watson hesitated again. "Sergeant Watson will explain that to you."

"Who? Your son?" Butch guessed.

Dr. Watson grinned a half-hearted grin. "No, nothing like that. We have the same last name but we're not in any way related. He's a sergeant with the Norristown police. They're here investigating. Your sister and brother are next door with some neighbors."

Butch was terribly confused. "Police in our house? What for?"

The bedroom door opened and in came a large man in a uniform. He had a moon face as kindly as Dr. Watson's, and to Butch's considerable amazement, his skin was black. Butch had seen black people on TV---many of the wrestlers and boxers were black---but he had never been close to a real, live black person before.

"This is Officer Watson," Dr. Watson said, and they nodded at each other and then Dr. Watson nodded at Butch. "He likes to be called Butch."

"It's all right to talk to him?" Officer Watson said.

"His pulse is strong and except for the hives he seems fine," Dr. Watson said. Taking his black bag, he went around the bed to the door. "I'll be back to check on you tomorrow, Butch. A neighbor will be looking after you. Theresa Gordon. You know her, yes?"

Butch nodded. The Gordons were right next door. "Where are mom and dad?"

Officer Watson and Dr. Watson exchanged glances and Dr. Watson bowed his head and went out.

"I'm very sorry," Officer Watson said, moving to the side of the bed. "But I need to ask you some questions."

"Where are my mom and dad?" Butch repeated. This was all too weird.

Officer Watson took his hat off and wrung the brim in his hands. He looked very sad. "I wish I didn't have to be the one to break this to you but your mother is being questioned by the lieutenant so it's up to me." He took a deep breath. "Your father is dead."

"What?" Butch braced his elbows and managed to sit halfway up.

"Your father is dead," Officer Watson said again, and stood still as if waiting.

Butch's mind seemed to shut down. "But....," was all he could get out.

"Your mother says he collapsed in your kitchen after a night out drinking," Officer Watson said in a gentle kind of way. "The cause of death hasn't been determined yet. Dr. Watson says it could have been a heart attack or a stroke although that would be unusual for a man your dad's age. He was only thirty-three."

Butch had heard about heart attacks but he had no idea what a stroke was. All he could think of was 'Dad dead?' over and over. He knew what dead was. He had seen dead animals at the side of the road and knew that dead people were buried in the church cemetery.

"I'm so sorry," Officer Watson was saying. "We'll know more once the autopsy is completed."

"The what?"

Office Watson winced and quickly said, "I need to ask a few questions. Were you by any chance awake when your dad came home?"

"No," Butch said. Which was true. He woke up

after, when they were fighting. It all came back to him in a rush and he thought for a moment he might burst into tears but he held it in.

"Again, I'm so sorry to have to ask," Officer Watson said. "But did you hear anything last night? Anything out of the ordinary?" Officer Watson stopped as if catching himself.

"I don't think so," Butch said.

Officer Watson cleared his throat and put his hat back on. "Well, that's all I need for now. You rest. I understand you're very ill."

Finally alone, Butch lay back and stared at the ceiling. His dad was *gone*. He didn't have a father anymore. Unbidden, a memory popped into his head. Of one of the times he watched his dad take a bath and they talked about everything under the sun.

On that day---exactly how it came up Butch couldn't recall---they had talked about his mom's dad dying while mowing the lawn, and at one point his own dad stopped washing and become super serious.

"Listen to me, son. If something ever happens to me, you'll be the man of the family."

"I will?"

"Of course. You need to give me your word that you'll look after your mom and your sister and brother."

"Sure, dad."

"There's nothing more important in life than looking out for those you love. Do you understand?"

"I understand," Butch assured him.

"You give me your word? You promise?"

"I promise."

Now the bedroom door opened and Butch thought it would be one of the Watsons' but it was his mother and Theresa Gordon. His mom had been crying and her cheeks were wet with tears and she dabbed at them as she came and sat on the bed and held out her arms for a hug.

"I have stuff on me," Butch said.

"I know," his mother said. "Have they explained things to you? About your dad, I mean? I have to leave, son. They're taking me to the station for more questioning..."

"Station?"

"The police station. Theresa has offered to look after you while I'm gone. I don't know how long it will be but hopefully not too long."

"It's horrible," Theresa said. She was a smallish woman with the nicest smile and a button nose and had three children of her own. Her husband was a steel worker. "Making you go there after all you've been through."

"They have to follow the letter of the law," his mother said. She hugged Butch a second time and kissed him on the head. "Be good."

"I will," Butch said.

"I can watch him until eleven," Theresa said. "Jim wants me home by then."

At the door his mother blew him a kiss and they were gone.

Butch sank into the pillow and tried to think. Now that he was the man of the house what should he be doing? His head still felt yucky and he was so very tired that although he tried to stay awake, a veil descended.

Sounds woke him. The room was dark and he called out, "Theresa?"

"It's me," said a voice so softly he hardly heard her. "Mom?"

There was rustling and Butch felt the bed move. A night light came on. His mother was buttoning her robe. Her eyes were wet and her whole body slumped with exhaustion. "Sorry I woke you. I just got home. It's after midnight. They kept me at the station over ten hours." She pulled back the cover on her side of the bed. "If you don't mind, we'll sleep together tonight. I should sleep on the couch but I just don't want to."

"It's fine, mom," Butch said. She looked so worn out that he felt tears begin to fill his eyes but he blinked them away. Men didn't cry and he was the man of the house now.

She got into bed and turned with her back to him and curled into a ball. Suddenly she sat up and glanced over her shoulder. "Wait. What about you? Need anything? Something to eat? Something to drink? Do you need to go to the bathroom?"

"I'm fine," Butch said. "Just tired."

His mom smiled and bent to kiss him and curled up once more with her back to him. "We'll sleep then. Goodnight son."

"Mom?"

"I'd rather not talk right now if that's okay. This has been the worst day of my life. Even worse than when my mom died."

'You're not going to die, are you?"

"What? No. I can't. Who would look after you and your sister and your brother? Now go to sleep."

"Is it all over now? The bad stuff?"

"I hope so."

It wasn't.

Two days later the police were back.

By then the strange hives were fading and Butch could get around on his own. His sister and brother were back and they were all in the living room watching *Popeye Theater* with Sally Starr on TV when there was a loud knock on the front door.

It was three policemen. One was Sergeant Watson. Another, Butch overheard, was a Captain. They didn't appear friendly like before.

"Mrs. Robbins," the captain said. "I'm afraid we need to take you in for more questioning."

Butch's mom moved near to the couch and to Bruce and his siblings. "Now? I answered every question you had. More than once."

"It appears you weren't entirely honest with us," the captain said.

"How so?" his mother demanded.

"You told us that Albert collapsed and you had no idea why."

"So?"

"So the autopsy has revealed that your husband was shot."

Butch's mother appeared dumbfounded.

"How is it you failed to mention that?" the captain asked.

Butch's mother didn't answer.

"You told us the two of you had an argument and he got up and collapsed. You said that you thought he passed out from being intoxicated. Yet his blood alcohol content wasn't that high. And now the coroner finds a bullet in his gut...."

"Please!" his mother said, placing her hand on Butch's sister. "Think of the children!"

"You need to get ready to go," the captain said. "If you don't have anyone who can look after them...."

"I do," his mother said. "My friend next door. She will."

"Get hold of her. Now."

Butch was angry that the captain was being so stern. He smiled at Sergeant Watson who smiled back.

Theresa Gordon came in somewhat out of breath and she was hardly through the door when the police escorted Butch's mother out. His sister began crying and Theresa comforted her.

Butch was left on his own. He went out on the front porch and watched the police car leave. He could see the back of his mother's head through the rear window. She didn't look back or wave or anything.

The afternoon waned and evening came and went and still their mother didn't return. Along about eight the phone rang and Theresa answered and came into the living room to let them know that their mom wouldn't be home until well after their bedtime so she would see to tucking them in.

Butch slept fitfully that night. His insides were in turmoil. He was trying to be the man of the house as his dad told him to be. He was trying to be tough as he should. But he kept asking himself, *What did all this mean?* Why did his dad have to die? Why did God *let* his dad die? In Sunday school they taught that God loved everyone and if you prayed to God---as Butch did every night because his mother insisted on him saying his prayers before he went to sleep---God would watch over you.

Butch had prayed when his dad and mom were arguing. He had prayed as he never prayed before. He had asked God to make them stop and for everything to be fine but now his dad was dead and his mom was with the police and everything was topsy-turvy.

At long last he drifted off. He was first up, not much after sunrise, and padded out to the kitchen expecting to find Theresa.

His mother was at the kitchen table. Her head was bowed and her whole body slumped and he thought he heard her sniffle.

"Mom?"

She slowly looked up. Her eyes were red and her face wasn't as it should be. It was drawn and haggard and there was little life in it. "David," she said.

"Are you all right?"

"No," his mother said. "I'll be honest with you. I'll never be all right again."

"What happened with the police?"

"They questioned me until two in the morning and brought me home. I go back in later for more questioning."

"What? Why?"

"I'll explain later. I'm too tired right now. Can you fix cereal for yourself? I need to catch a little sleep before your brother and sister are up."

"Sure."

Butch watched her wearily head down the hall.

Instead of making his breakfast he went out on the front porch and sat in the morning chill and clasped his arms about himself and shivered. He looked up at the sky, wishing he could see God and they could talk face to face about the awful things that were happening.

Instead he saw the Three Stooges.

AFTER HE WENT INSANE

On her TV show every weekday afternoon, Sally Starr featured the Three Stooges along with Popeye.

Butch loved the Stooges. They made him laugh more than anything. He most liked the combination of Moe, Larry and Curly. Shemp was funny and Joe too but they weren't Curly.

He would lie on the floor with his chin in his hands in rapt attention and roll with mirth at their antics.

At the beginning of each short film, the images of the Three Stooges were shown while music played. Just their heads. Moe, Curly, and Larry.

Butch never expected to see those images in the sky. He looked away and back again but they were still there. And they were huge, a hundred times bigger than on TV. He blinked and shook his head but they didn't go away.

"This isn't real," he said aloud. "It can't be."

The faces stared down at him.

"What are you doing up there?" Butch said.

"You wanted answers, kid," Moe said, sounding just like the real Moe on TV.

"This isn't funny," Butch said. "My dad died."

"Nyuk, Nyuk, Nyuk," Curly said, and he, too, sounded just like the real Curly.

"That wasn't nice," Butch said.

"Life isn't always nice," Larry said. He sounded

55

exactly like the real Larry and more than a little sad, as if he sympathized. "You found that out the hard way."

Butch bowed his chin and shivered. "Go away."

"We can't go away until you send us, kid," Moe said.

"You brought us here," Larry said. "We're the answers to the questions you have."

"You're the Stooges," Butch said. "You make people laugh. What do you know about anything?"

"Nyuk, Nyuk, Nyuk," Curly said.

Butch closed his eyes and shook his head and refused to look at them or say anything for the longest while. When at last he peeked up they were still there. "Go away, darn you."

"Ask," Moe said.

"We're waiting on you," Larry said.

"This is stupid," Butch muttered.

"Nyuk, Nyuk, Nyuk," Curly said.

Butch flared with anger and stood up. "All right. I'll ask a question. Why did God let my dad die?"

"Hold out your hands, kid," Moe said.

"What?"

"Hold out your hands," Moe said again.

Butch did as he was told.

"Now pick one," Larry said.

Butch raised his right arm.

"There you go, kid," Moe said.

"Now you have your answer," Larry said.

"What kind of answer was that?" Butch demanded.

"The only answer life gives," Larry said.

"That makes no sense," Butch said, becoming angry.

"It's the only answer there is, kid," Moe said.

"It eludes most," Larry said. "You're lucky."

Butch bunched his fists. "I'm lucky my dad is dead?"

"Nyuk, Nyuk, Nyuk," Curly said.

Butch was so mad he wished he could hit him.

"Who are you talking to, son?"

Startled, Butch turned.

His mother was staring at him through the screen door. She had her robe on and her hair was dishevelled. "I'm having a hard time sleeping and I heard you."

"No one," Butch blurted.

"You're talking to yourself? That's a bad habit to get into."

"I won't do it again."

She tiredly smiled and left.

Butch stared at the sky. The Three Stooges were still there, staring back. *Can I talk to you in my head?* he thought.

Sure, kid," Moe said.

We're in your head too, Larry said.

Curly, of course, said *Nyuk, Nyuk, Nyuk.*

Butch crossed his forearms over his knees and rested his elbows on them. *I don't get any of this. You're not real and yet......*

Pick one of yours hands again, kid, Moe said.

Take a deep breath, Larry said.

Butch waited but Curly didn't say 'Nyuk, Nyuk, Nyuk.' *What is it you want to tell me?*

No, kid, Moe *said.*

What is it you want to tell you?" Larry said.

Why my dad had to die, Butch said.

57

Had to, kid?" Moe said.

Nothing is ever had to, Larry said. Except when it is.

Nyuk, Nyuk, Nyuk, Curley said.

Butch shook his head. *This is crazy.*

Don't let words confuse you, kid, Moe said.

They're just sounds, Larry said. *Sounds aren't the thing.*

At a total loss, Butch said, *Why did God let my dad die?*

Let or do, kid?" Moe said.

God does, Larry said. *Except when God doesn't.*

God isn't to blame for my dad, Butch said. *He didn't pull the trigger.*

No 'He', kid, Moe said.

No 'She', either, Larry said.

Curly winked.

Butch'wanted desperately to understand. *In Sunday School they tell us God loves us. How can God loves us if God lets us die like my dad died?*

Didn't you learn anything from picking a hand, kid? Moe said.

God picked a hand a long time ago, Larry said.

Everyone dies, kid, Moe said.

Or they don't, Larry said.

Butch sat up. *I get it now. You're teasing me. None of this real. None of this is serious.*

We're as serious as can be, kid, Moe said.

We're the Three Stooges, Larry said.

Nyuk, Nyuk, Nyuk, Curley said.

Frowning, Butch stood. *Enough. I don't want to talk to you anymore.*

When you change your mind we'll be here, kid, Moe said.

Just for you, Larry said.

Butch looked at Curly but Curly didn't say anything. Frustrated, he went inside and spent the morning with his sister and brother.

Theresa came over to look after them.

His mother didn't get up until the middle of the afternoon. She was red-eyed and in misery. Sitting on the couch, she called Butch and then Karen over and gave each of them a tight hug. She did the same with baby Mark.

Later the *Times-Herald* was delivered. Theresa brought it in and opened it. "There's something about you," she said to Becky.

"Read it. Please."

Theresa smoothed the newspaper. "***Man Found Dead Of Gunshot Wound.***"

Butch's mom closed her eyes and seemed to sway. "Go on."

"**A 33-year old East Norriton father of three young children, found in the kitchen of his home this morning, died of a gunshot wound of the abdomen, an autopsy disclosed. Albert Robbins of Trooper Lane, East of Trooper Road, was pronounced dead by Dr. James Watson, of Norristown, who was called to the home by the man's wife, Beatrice Detwiler Robbins. It was reported it first was believed Robbins had been stricken and collapsed to the floor of the kitchen. However. Dr. John C. Simpson, Coroner, when notified of the death, ordered an autopsy. At Montgomery Hospital, the bullet wound was** discovered and a .22 calibre slug recovered from the body, he said. Joining the investigation after the cause of death was determined, East Norriton Police Chief James Oliver began questioning Mrs. Robbins to obtain further details of the death. He said a gun was found on the kitchen table, near where the body was found sprawled on the floor. Dr. Simpson said a certificate of death will be withheld until completion of the investigation. Mr Robbins was the father of three children, David, Karen and Mark."

Butch hadn't realized the newspaper would tell everyone about his dad's death. Since his mom wasn't saying much, he made it a point to be waiting for the newspaper boy the next day so he could read it before anyone else. He hoped there would be more. He wasn't disappointed.

In bold print a banner headline read, **DARED HER TO SHOOT, BUT WIFE SAYS GUN DISCHARGE ACCIDENT**.

Butch didn't remember hearing a shot. Guns made a loud noise. As their rifle did when his dad would take him target shooting. He read on.

'Mrs. Albert L. Robbins, East Norriton, Admits Pushing Gun Aside; Didn't Know Her Spouse Was Shot. The accidental discharge of a .22 calibre rifle which he placed on a kitchen table and then allegedly "dared" his wife to shoot caused the death of Albert L. Robbins, East Norriton, yesterday, authorities disclosed after a five-hour investigation.'

Butch stopped reading. He didn't hear his dad say anything like that. Then again, he couldn't hear everything they said. He bent to the newspaper.

'According to Beatrice Detwiler Robbins, 30, her husband returned to their Trooper Lane home about 3 A.M. yesterday. She said he had been drinking heavily and went immediately to the bedroom and carried the rifle to the kitchen. Placing it on the table, he placed one of his hands on the stock and the other on the trigger, telling her to shoot. Mrs. Robbins told Chief County Detective Charles G. Moody, East Norriton Police Chief James Oliver and other investigators her husband had performed the same "prank" on previous occasions.'

Butch stopped reading again. He never saw or heard his dad do anything like that. This was so strange. He continued.

'According to the police, she said she pushed the butt of the rifle away after telling Robbins to "go to bed". As she pushed the gun, she said, she heard a click and her husband dropped to the floor. Believing he was "faking", she again told him to go to bed and left the room. Returning to the kitchen a short time later, she noticed he apparently was ill. Believing this was caused by sickness due to drinking, she placed a towel under his head.'

Butch stopped. His poor dad. But why had the rifle clicked and not gone bang? He bent over the newspaper.

'Chief Moody said Mrs. Robbins apparently did not hear the report of the gunshot since the muzzle was against her husband's stomach. He said a test conducted at the District Attorney's office indicated the trigger would click if the gun was knocked aside. About 8:30 yesterday morning, Mrs. Robbins discovered her husband still was lying on the kitchen floor. She called Dr. James Watson, of Norristown, who pronounced him dead. Dr. John C. Simpson, Coroner, and Chief Oliver were called, but it was not until an autopsy was being performed at Montgomery Hospital, shortly before noon, that the bullet was discovered. Mrs. Robbins was questioned in the District Attorney's office from about 3 until 8 last night. Present were Chiefs Moody and Oliver, East Norriton Officer Charles Belitto and County Detectives. Both Chiefs said Mrs. Robbins told them her husband, an employe of Taylor Fibre Co., Betzwood, previously had handed her a loaded revolver or a knife and dared her to kill him. They said she was unaware the bullet had caused death until after learning of the autopsy finding. Chief Moody said there was very little blood from the abdomen wound. According to Chiefs Moody and Oliver they are satisfied the death was caused by the accidental discharge. They are making a full report to Dr. Simpson today and will recommend Mrs. Robbins be held on a technical charge of manslaughter until after a Coroner's Inquest. The victim was father of three children, David, Karen and Mark. Mr. Robbins' parents live on W. Marshall St., West Norriton. Also surviving are two brothers.'

Butch set the paper down and sat back. His dad wanted his mom to kill him? Not once but a bunch of times? That didn't sound like his dad at all. His dad never talked about dying and killing himself. Or would he only talk about that to her?

The next several days were a blur. People came and went. Neighbors. Friends. Others Butch didn't know.

Strangely, his dad's parents and brothers didn't come.

The newspaper churned out stories.

The next let Butch know that his mother had been released on bond, whatever that was. Also that his dad's funeral was to be held on the upcoming Saturday. He knew about funerals. It was where they buried dead people.

Dozens came, among them his father's side of the family. They sat apart and didn't talk to his mom or to him.

The viewing was open casket. His mom went up and cried and his sister went up and cried.

When it was his turn, Butch walked to the coffin and stood staring at his father's face. His dad looked so pale. Butch stood there a long while, knowing it was the last time he would ever set eyes on his father. He told himself to remember this moment, to never forget it for as long as he lived.

When he turned he saw his dad's mom and dad in the next section. She was crying. His dad's dad smiled at him. His dad's brothers didn't look at him.

Butch went down the aisle to the pew where his mom sat with his sister and brother. He sat straight, his shoulders high, staring at the casket.

"You're not crying?" his mom said softly so only he heard.

"No," Butch said.

"Why not? That's your father. Aren't you upset that he's gone?"

"I'm doing what he said to do," Butch said.

"What's that?"

"Being the man of the family."

"Oh, son."

"A man should be tough."

His mother dabbed at tears and gently placed her arm around him. "Listen to me. You're a boy. Not a man. And even the toughest of men cry."

Butch went on staring at the casket.

"You can if you need to. No one will hold it against you."

"No," Butch said almost fiercely. He felt pride in doing as his dad taught him. He refused to show weakness. He wouldn't cry. He would hold it in.

Along about the second week after the burial, Butch's mom got a phone call from his dad's mom. His dad's parents wanted Butch to come spend the night. Butch heard his mom's end of the conversation and she didn't sound happy about the idea but she finally gave in and agreed that Butch could stay over on Friday night.

Late Friday afternoon, not long before his mom was to take him over, she ushered Butch out onto the back steps.

"We need to talk, son."

"Okay."

"An adult talk."

Butch wondered what the difference was between that and their usual talks. "Okay."

"You're going over to your father and mother in-law's in a while."

"NaNa's and PopPop's. I know. To spend the night."

His mom squatted and put both her hands on his

shoulders and looked into his eyes. "Listen close. If they do or say anything that makes you uncomfortable, you're to let me know right away."

"Huh?" Butch said.

"They might ask you questions. About your dad. About the night he died. Those sorts of things."

"Oh." To Butch that seemed perfectly right for them to do.

"You're not to say a word about it."

"Mom?"

"Tell them you don't want to talk about it. Any questions they have, they can ask me. Understand?"

No, Butch didn't, and he hesitated.

"Do you understand?" his mom repeated, giving his shoulders a hard squeeze. "I've told them that talking about it will upset you too much and they're not to do it."

"Okay," Butch said.

"Not one word, you hear?"

"Yes."

On the drive to Norristown his mom kept glancing over at him. When they were only a few blocks from Marshall Street she pulled to the curb and faced him. "Do you remember our talk?"

"Of course," Butch said.

She bent closer. "I don't trust them. The truth is, they've never liked me. It won't surprise me if they break their promise and badger you with questions and I won't have that. It's not fair to you."

Butch didn't say anything.

"So here's what we're going to do." His mom pointed toward the end of the street. "Do you see that phone booth?"

Butch nodded. It was broad daylight. How could he not see it?"

His mom opened her handbag and took out a coin purse and fished out a quarter. "Take this." She held it out to him.

"What's it for?" Butch asked.

"The phone booth. What else? Keep it in your pocket and don't let them know you have it. If they start asking questions about your dad dying, anything at all about that night, I want you to sneak out and get to that phone booth and call me and let me know."

"Sneak out?" Butch said in amazement.

His mom nodded.

"From NaNa's and PopPop's?"

His mom nodded a second time. "You call and I'll come fetch you right away. We're not going to let them take advantage of you being a child. You don't want that either, right?"

Butch bobbed his chin even though he was unsure what he was agreeing to.

"Put the quarter in your pocket and whatever you do, don't lose it." His mom took a slip of paper from her purse. "Take this too. It's our phone number."

"I know our number," Butch said. She had made him memorize it long ago.

She shook the slip. "Take it anyway. I won't risk you forgetting."

Butch slid it into his pocket with the coin. "How do I use a phone booth?" He'd never done it before.

His mother gave him instructions. She gripped the steering wheel to go but paused and turned. "You might think this is strange, me asking you to sneak out on them. I have a good reason. It wouldn't surprise me at all if they try to take you and your brother and sister away from me."

Butch was shocked. "Your our mom. They can't do that."

"Under the law they can. If they convince a judge I'm an unfit mother, they can take you and Karen and Mark away. Do you want that?"

Butch felt a wave of fear shoot through him. He'd already lost his dad. He didn't want to lose his mom, too. "No. Never."

Nana and PopPop were waiting on the front porch. Nana greeted Butch with a hug and fussed over him. PopPop took his overnight bag.

His mom didn't stay long. Nana asked how she was doing and his mom said as well as could be expected. Then she hugged and kissed Butch, gave him a meaningful look, and left.

"We can't tell you how happy you've made us," PopPop said as she drove off.

Butch was ushered to his room. It had wooden floors and a glass cabinet that NaNa cautioned he mustn't touch because it was filled with her 'knicknacks'. Among them was a porcelain polar bear he liked very much.

They gave him the run of the house, the driveway and the yard. The driveway reminded him of a time when he was younger and his dad and him had their photo taken by his mom, standing in front of PopPop's car.

The driveway bordered a high wrought-iron fence.

Beyond was a yard as wide as a foodball field and a great, grand house that belonged to rich people.

Butch once talked to the boy who lived there, each on their respective sides of the fence. Butch asked what it was like to be rich and the boy said his mother was always buying him new clothes he didn't want to wear.

They would have talked longer but the rich boy's mother came out and called the boy in.

For supper that evening Nana served chicken and mashed potatoes and corn, one of Butch's favorite meals. Not once did NaNa or PopPop ask about his dad and the night his dad died.

Butch was having a fine time.

"What would you like for dessert?" PopPop wanted to know.

"I have ice cream," NaNa said.

Butch laughed and held up his spoon. "Ice cream will do great."

NaNa excused herself.

"Are you happy, David?" PopPop asked.

"Happy how?" Butch said.

"With your dad gone, being with your mom?"

Butch was at a loss as to how 'happy' had anything to do with it.

"If you're not, you could come live with us, you know."

His mother's warning shot through Butch like a bolt of lightning. He didn't respond and was glad when NaNa returned bearing a bowl which she placed in front of him. To hide his unease Butch dug in. He barely noticed the ice cream was pink. Not until he swallowed several spoonfuls did it occur to him that the ice cream was, "Strawberry! I love strawberry! Thanks."

"Eat it a lot, do you?" PopPop said.

"Now and then." Butch was on his fifth spoonful already.

"Oh my! Wait!" NaNa exclaimed. "I forgot. You shouldn't be eating that. Your mom says you're allergic to strawberry. It gives you hives."

"That's all right, NaNa," Butch said. "I never had hives until that one time."

"You don't say," PopPop said.

Their expressions caused Butch to stiffen. They were smiling but he sensed something wasn't right.

"You never had hives before the night Albert died?" NaNa said.

"No," Butch admitted.

"That's strange, don't you think?" PopPop said. "Surely you would remember a thing like hives?"

"Why did your mother say you did?" NaNa said.

Butch stopped eating. He had lost his appetite. "Maybe I shouldn't then."

"Would you care to talk about that night?" PopPop asked.

"No."

"We have a few questions," NaNa said. "Things that strike us as peculiar."

"Mom says I shouldn't talk about it."

"She told you not to?" PopPop said.

Butch didn't see the harm in telling the truth. "She said I shouldn't no matter what."

PopPop and NaNa looked at each other and NaNa's eyes misted and her lower lip quivered.

"I told you," she said.

PopPop bowed his head. "It's unthinkable. And yet...."

Butch was happy they let the subject drop. After supper they watched a little TV and NaNa trucked Butch off to bed. He lay listening to the TV and their hushed voices and all he could think about was being taken away from his mom. After an interminable length the TV went off and he heard them climb the stairs. He closed his eyes, pretending to be asleep. His door opened and he cracked his eyelids to see that NaNa had poked her head in. She stared at him quite a while and quietly closed the bedroom door again.

Butch let a lot of time go by. He needed to be sure they were asleep. A snore convinced him they were. Slipping out of bed, he padded to the door.

The house was mostly dark and completely still save for the ticking of the grandfather clock on the mantle.

Butch was in his blue pajamas. He didn't change into his clothes but he did put his slippers on. Taking the quarter from his pants, he crept down the stairs. The living room was a sea of shadow.

By the clock it was close to midnight.

Butch crept to the front door. Every step, he expected the lights to flash on and NaNa and PopPop to demand what he was up to.

A hinge on the front door squeaked loudly when he opened it. He froze, afraid they heard, but nothing happened.

Night claimed the neighborhood. Here and there dogs barked.

The phone booth was over a block away. In the

daytime that hadn't seemed so far but now it seemed somehow sinister.

Butch glanced both ways and padded off the porch and along the driveway. The air was chill and he broke out in goosebumps. He also broke into a run.

His link to his mother---the quarter--he clenched so tightly, his hand hurt.

Gravel crunched under his slippers. A dog in a fenced yard growled.

He reached the phone booth and pulled on the door and recoiled at the loud noise it made. Not only that, a light came on inside, revealing him to the world. Or to NaNa and PopPop should they happen to look out their window. Slipping in, he shut the door.

And froze.

A man was coming up the street.

Butch crouched, his breath catching in his throat. Why would anyone be out so late? Had the man seen him and was coming to ask what he was up to? Fighting down his worry, he watched the man come along the sidewalk and go past without so much as a glance in the booth's direction.

Butch breathed again. He stood and reminded himself of his mother's instructions. Lift the receiver. Insert the quarter into the slot. Wait for the dial tone. Dial the number.

The first ring at the other end was cut short by his mom.

"Butch?"

"It's me," he confirmed. "They did as you said. They asked a lot of questions. Mostly about the strawberry ice cream. They gave me some."

"I knew it!" his mom said. "I knew it, I knew it, I knew it!"

"They even asked if I wanted to be theirs."

"I'm on my way to get you."

"What do I do? Wait in the phone booth?"

"No. Sneak back into their house and up to your bedroom. Can you do that without being caught?"

"I can try."

"You do it, you hear me? And don't worry. Mommy is on her way!"

There was a click and the dial tone and Butch stared at the phone and hung up. Easing the booth door open, he glanced both ways. There was no sign of the man.

Butch started to run and caught himself. Running might draw attention. He forced himself to stroll along as if it were the most normal thing in the world for him to be out and about so late. When he reached the driveway his nerves couldn't take it any longer and he raced to the front door and opened it as quietly as possible. He didn't let himself relax even a little until he was safe in bed with the blanket pulled to his chin.

Sleep was impossible. He lay listening to the clock and the occasional dog and now and again a snore.

When car lights played over his window he suspected it was his mom. He was proven right by loud banging on the front door. Voices sounded, and he heard PopPop and NaNa go past his room wondering who in the world it could be.

Louder voices ensued. Butch's mom and his grandparents were arguing. He couldn't catch everything they said. It might be they didn't want him to hear. He got that his mom was demanding to take him home and they were objecting.

The bedroom door swept open and his mom stormed in, saying, "Let's go. Are you packed and ready?"

"I'm in my PJ's," Butch said.

"You're not dressed yet?" She gestured angrily. "Hurry up about it. I'm not staying in this house a minute longer than I have to."

PopPop and NaNa stood in the living room and watched them leave, PopPop with his arm around NaNa. PopPop looked sad. NaNa looked mad.

His mother waited until they were almost to Trooper Road to smile at him and remark, "You did good back there. I'm proud of you."

"It was wrong of them to ask those things?"

"It's wrong to bring your dad's death up ever again. Not just them but anyone. From here on out, we never discuss it and we don't let anyone else talk about it, either. Understand?"

Butch did and he didn't. Yes, it was upsetting to bring it up. But never, ever? That would be as if he never had a dad, and he did, and loved him dearly.

There was no one he could share his feelings with. Certainly not his mom. Nor his PopPop and NaNa. His sister was too young, his brother couldn't even talk yet.

So it was that the next day, when he sat outside on the front step and gazed skyward, he was pleased to see three familiar faces gazing down at him. *I'm glad you're here.*

We don't have a say, kid, Moe said.

73

It's you, not us, Larry said.

Nyuk, Nyuk, Nyuk, Curley said.

I used to think you were the funniest, Butch said, mildly peeved. To Larry he said, *You know about last night?*

We know what you know, Larry replied.

Mares eat oats and does eat oats, Moe said.

What does that mean?" Butch thought. *Why did my NaNa and PopPop do that?*

They love you, kid, Moe said.

Your mother, not so much, Larry said.

Nyuk, Nyuk, Nyuk.

Things are so messed up, Butch said. *I'm supposed to be the man of the family and fix them. But how?*

You can't be a man until you are, kid, Moe said.

Larry said, *A lot of people go through life being someone else. Don't get into the habit.*

Nyuk, Nyuk, Nyuk.

What do I do? Butch beseeched them.

Be you, kid, Moe said.

Pick hands as you need to, Larry said. *It's the greatest gift we're given.*

Short of life, kid, Moe said.

Along about the fifth week Butch opened the newspaper and was riveted by a headline. **WIDOW IS HELD IN GUN DEATH OF HER SPOUSE**. It went on to say that a Coroner's Inquest had been held, and a jury ruled that his mom should be held on a charge of involuntary manslaughter. She had posted bond so she could stay free until a Grand Jury took up the case. Chief Moody reported that the rifle had been sent to the F.B.I. laboratory and the F.B.I. had determined that the rifle had a 'hair trigger' that could be actuated by the slightest nudge.

Butch knew about the F.B.I. They were the best in the world at what they did. This meant his mom was telling the truth and the shooting wasn't her fault.

Weeks passed.

Summer heat held sway.

If Butch thought enough bad things had happened, he shouldn't have to experience more, he was mistaken.

Along about August he was standing with two friends near the family's vegetable garden. One of his friends pointed and said, "Look at that rabbit! It's eating our lettuce!"

Butch looked. "What rabbit?" All he saw was a brownish lump.

"Right there!" His friend jabbed the air with his finger. "Are you blind or something?"

The older brother cocked his head. "You really can't see it?"

Butch squinted but all he could make out was the dark blob. "No."

"You better let your mom know," the older boy said. "Something must be wrong with your eyes."

It was.

A visit to the eye doctor resulted in Butch having to wear black horn-rimmed glasses. His mother expressed surprise. No one on her side of the family or on his father's side wore glasses except for PopPop and he only had to wear them late in life.

"I wonder," she said as she rubbed his head in sympathy.

She never explained what she wondered about.

School started. To Butch's surprise, the teacher assigned another boy, Gerald Zeigler, to 'look after him', as she put it, and keep him constant compay the first couple of weeks.

When Butch said he didn't need looking after, his teacher stated that she knew all about 'his situation', and this was her way of showing him that people cared.

Gerry was big and friendly and easy to get along with---but some of the other kids whispered and pointed.

Butch became down in the dumps, which was rare for him. He didn't laugh. He seldom smiled. Until the tenth of September when another *Times-Herald* story broke the good news: **Charge Against Mother Of Three Ignored In Death Of Spouse**. He avidly read that 'a charge of involuntary manslaughter against a 30-year old East Norriton mother of three children was ignored by the September Grand Jury early this afternoon resulting in the freeing of Beatrice D. Robbins, of Trooper Lane.

Butch could have whooped for joy.

He read on. '**The Grand Jury reached its decision of "not a true bill" after hearing testimony of East Norriton Police Chief James Oliver who, with Chief County Detective Charles G. Moody, had investigated the death.**'

Further down he read again that his mom had '**told them her husband, an employee of Taylor Fibre Co., Betzwood, had handed her a loaded revolver or a knife on other occasions and "dared" her to kill him.**'

Why was it, Butch wondered, that he never heard or saw his dad do anything like that? Why *would* his dad do that? His dad seemed happy about life. He even had plans to start his own sanitation company and work at that full time.

Then again, Butch was a kid, and adults didn't always tell kids things.

Still, the worst was over.

Later that afternoon he was on the front step and the faces of the Three Stooges filled the sky and stared down at him but they didn't say anything until he piped up with, *Did you hear the good news?*

That your dad is dead, kid? Moe said.

And your mom shot him? Larry said.

Nyuk, Nyuk, Nyuk. From Curley.

It wasn't mom's fault, Butch said. *It's in the newspaper. She bumped the gun and it went off and killed him. She didn't mean to do it.*

*So you're back to God killed your dad, kid,"*Moe said.

I never said that, Butch said. *I said God let it happen. That's not the same thing.*

It isn't, kid? Moe said.

You sure? Larry said.

Hear me out, Butch said, and put his train of thought to words. *God lets people be born. They live a while and then they die. God doesn't let them live forever.*

So? Larry said.

So dying is part of life. And if that's true, then in a way, God lets everyone and everything have life just so they'll die.

Oh, kid, Moe said.

I was wrong, Butch said. *In a way, God kills us.*

God kills everything.

Circles within circles, Larry said.

Am I right? Butch asked.

The Stooges stared.

I think I finally understand, Butch said. *Dying and killing are just part of life.*

Have it all figured out, do you kid? Moe said.

Or maybe you don't, Larry said.

I wonder what it's like to kill? Butch said.

Nyuk, Nyuk, Nyuk, Curly said.

LITTLE BOY BLUE

His mother became a new woman. Gone were her red eyes. She no longer cried at night. She no longer walked around looking miserable. She smiled a lot and seemed happy and more like their mom of old.

She was especially happy, Butch learned, that the dropping of charges meant the insurance money could go through. His dad, it turned out, had life insurance in the amount of ten thousand dollars.

The check came and the first thing their mom did was buy new outfits for all of them and hire a photographer to come out to their house and take pictures of all of them for an album.

When Butch asked why they would spend money on something like that, his mother replied that it was a new beginning in their life.

Next she bought a used car. She got rid of the *Willys Jeep* their dad had liked and replaced it with a used *Ford Woodie* station wagon. It was much less cramped.

The school year went by and a new summer began. Butch was looking forward to having time to himself to play with his toys and explore the woods and all sorts of things.

Then his mother dropped two bombshells.

The first was that Butch and his siblings were

going to spend weekdays living with their great Aunt Evelyn and her husband Tyson on their farm up in Pennsylvania Dutch country. A lot of Amish and Old Mennonites had farms in the region, ladies who wore bonnets and long dresses and men who had beards and wore straw hats.

Butch had been to the farm a few times. He liked all the animals but some other aspects not so much.

For starters the place had an outhouse instead of a indoors toilet. The bathroom in the farmhouse didn't have one. No bathtub, either. Just a sink they washed in. They didn't even have indoor plumbing. Their water came from an outside pump near the kitchen and they carried it inside in buckets.

Which meant that if Butch needed to go after dark, he must take a flashlight and venture a good distance from the house and sit on a wooden seat and do his business.

His sister hated it. She especially hated that Evelyn and Tyson didn't use toilet paper. They used an old SEARS catalogue. To wipe, you tore pages out and dabbed.

The second bombshell was that his mom arranged for him to attend Worcester Summer Bible School, which was run by the Worcester Mennonite Church.

"You'll learn all about the Bible and God and everything!" his mother tried to excite him about the prospect.

"I already know about God," Butch said.

His mom bent and put her hand on his shoulder. "Listen, son. After everything I've been through, I need some time to myself. We'll have weekends together.

And all this is only until school starts. By then I'll have to look for a job and we'll all be back together."

"What will you do by yourself?"

"I'll keep busy," his mom said, and laughed.

Off to the farm they went. His mom drove them up early every Monday morning and picked them up early each Saturday.

The very first afternoon, Aunt Evelyn and Uncle Tyson sat him down and told him that on a farm, everyone worked. Adults had jobs to do and the children had chores. Butch would be given his own, and Aunt Evelyn and Uncle Tyson expected him to perform them without fail.

Next day they woke him up at 4 a.m.

Butch trudged out to the barn in Tyson's wake. Tyson was tall and lean and hardly ever spoke. Butch never saw him smile, never heard him laugh. Part of that might have to do with an incident years before when Tyson went out to the milk house to begin setting up for the day. He'd neglected to close the window the night before and was unaware a barn owl had found its way in until the owl attacked him. It flew at his face and clawed his eyes and his sight was never the same. Tyson could see, just not as well.

Over a dozen dairy cows were held in place by metal bars. Head yokes, Tyson called them. Butch learned that the cows were trained to return from the pasture each evening and enter the barn where Tyson would slide their heads into the yokes to keep them in place overnight. Then he would feed them.

Morning was when the milking was done. Tyson showed Butch how to squeeze and pull on the teats so the milk squirted out. It needed to be done just right. Because if you did it wrong, not only would the milk not squirt, it hurt the cow and the cow would kick you. Butch learned that the hard way.

Uncle Tyson handled most of the milking. He had another job for Butch. One of Butch's new daily chores.

Tyson gave him a big shovel with a square scoop and had Butch stand at one end of a long trough that ran the length of the barn behind the cows. The trough was the cow equivalent of the outhouse. All night long, whenever a cow had the urge, that was where the urge ended up.

A dozen cows made for a lot of poop and pee.

Butch's chore was to shovel it all into a wheelbarrow and push the wheelbarrow out to where the spreader was parked and then shovel the poop into the spreader. Once the spreader was full, Tyson would hitch up one of the tractors and take it out to a field to be used as fertilizer.

The poop itself lay in great circular gobs. Butch had once heard the term 'cow patties' and it fit.

Butch never imagined an animal could poop so much.

At first the reek was almost enough to make Butch gag. Holding his breath as much as possible, he set the edge of the shovel on the botton of the trough and pushed, thinking to scoop some of the poop right up. It wasn't that easy. The poop was heavier than it appeared. Especially the newer poop.

He stopped and frowned and wished he was anywhere but there.

Tyson was watching him. "Keep at it. We go in for

breakfast at six and it needs to be done by then. Plus the other chores you have to do first."

Those other chores included helping to carry pails of milk to the milkhouse and collecting all the eggs from the chicken coop. Aunt Evelyn had shown Butch how the day before. You slid your hand in under the hens real easy and slid the egg out. Some of the hens didn't mind. Some pecked you.

After shoveling all the cow poop and toting a lot of pails, Butch was tired and sore and wanted dearly to lie down and rest. But he had to gather the stupid eggs. It didn't help his mood any that Uncle Tyson said, "Hurry it up. We're not holding breakfast for you." as he went on to the house, leaving Butch to finish alone.

A basket was kept near the entry to the chicken coop. Butch entered, liking the smell of the straw on the floor and the chickens after the stink in the barn. He went from nest box to nest box, carefully retrieving the eggs so as not to break them.

The roosters were out in the barnyard but nine yellow baby chicks were flitting about. Tiny creatures, the kind Butch had seen sold in stores at Easter time, sometimes dyed all the colors of the rainbow.

Butch came to the last nest box. The hen tilted her head from side to side and regarded his outstretched hand much as he imagined she might regard a snake. She clucked loudly, and when he went to slide his hand under her, she struck hard, pecking as fast and as furious as she could. It hurt like the dickens.

Butch yelped and drew his hand back. "You stupid chicken!" He was hungry and aching and worried that if he took too long, he wouldn't get any breakfast. He tried again and the hen, more agitated than before, flew into a frenzy of pecking and clucking. He groped and found an egg and was pulling it out when she pecked so hard, he involuntarily jerked his hand back and his fingers opened and the egg fell to the floor and broke.

Aunt Evelyn had made it plain that a cardinal rule of egg gathering was to never break one. "Eggs are food on our table or money in the bank from those we sell to, so we always treat them as delicately as possible."

Butch stared at the yellow yolk oozing from the split shell---and punched the chiken. She squawked and pecked and tried to come out of the box but he pushed her back and stormed to the door and began to close it. For two cents he would have strangled her.

The door was old, the wood unpainted, its hinges made of leather that had cracked and caused the door to hang lopsided. The bottom scraped the floor, which forced Butch to set down the egg basket and lift the door to swing it shut. As he was doing so a baby chick tried to slip out between the door and the jamb. He kicked to drive it back.

Butch put his shoulder to the door and this time almost had it closed when the baby chick thrust its head into the gap.

"No!" Butch said. "Get back." One of the rules was that the chickens weren't allowed out until ten or so.

The door caught the baby chick by the neck. It couldn't squeeze through or pull itself back. It was stuck and wildly chirped and struggled.

A new impulse came over Butch. A sensation of sheer pleasure shot through his body from his head to his toes. Tingling all over, Butch slowly---ever so slowly---pushed the door shut. The baby chick's chirps became shrill, its efforts frantic.

The chick went limp and Butch stopped pushing. The tingling continued, an almost indescribable pleasure.

Picking the baby chick up, he held it in the palm of his hand. He flicked the head with the tip of his finger and the head flopped from side to side. He flicked it again and yet again.

"So this is what it's like to kill," Butch said aloud. He wondered if this was how God killed. Or when God let someone die, as God had let his dad be shot.

He put the dead chick under some straw where it wouldn't be noticed, shut the door, grabbed the basket, and hurried to the farm house for his breakfast.

Aunt Evelyn was busy at the stove. The kitchen smelled of eggs and oatmeal and coffee, wonderful aromas after the cow trough. "How was your first morning as a farmer?" she asked with a twinkle in her eyes.

"More fun than I thought it would be."

"That's good," Aunt Evelyn said.

From his chair across the table Tyson said sternly, "Work isn't supposed to be fun. Work is supposed to be work."

"He's just a boy," Aunt Evelyn said.

"I was a boy once," Tyson said, "and I knew the difference between work and play."

"Yes, dear," Aunt Evelyn said.

Butch liked her, a lot. She was short and plump and always wore dresses down to her shoes and a small bonnet. He asked her about that once and she said it was called a prayer cap. He was puzzled as to what the cap had to do with prayer and she said it came from the Bible, from *1 Corinthians*.

Aunt Evelyn spent a lot of her time each day in the kitchen preparing three meals. When she wasn't cooking she was cleaning. Her only indulgence, as she called it, was an hour each afternoon she spent in front of their TV watching *As The World Turns*.

That TV was their only concession to modern times. And the only reason Tyson bought one was so he could watch baseball. He was a keen Philadelphia Phillies fan. The only other thing the pair watched were the nightly news.

Once Butch asked why they didn't watch movies or any of the regular shows and Aunt Evelyn replied that she stopped going to movies years ago and most TV shows weren't much different.

"Why did you stop?" Butch asked.

"I saw what they were trying to do," Aunt Evelyn said. "How they try to make you think like them."

Butch didn't see anything wrong with thinking like Robin Hood or the Lone Ranger but he kept the notion to himself.

The next morning the milking took longer than usual and Uncle Tyson told Butch to go on to breakfast and he would bring the eggs.

Butch and his sister had just started on their oatmeal when Tyson opened the kitchen door and told Evelyn he needed to speak to her outside. When they returned, they stood near the table and Evelyn held out her hands. In them was the dead baby chick.

Karen let out a gasp. "Is it dead? What happened

to it?"

"That's what we would like to know," Aunt Evelyn said, staring at Butch. "Uncle Tyson just found it in the coop."

Butch spooned oatmeal into his mouth. He loved oatmeal covered in sugar with cold milk.

"Any idea how it died, Butch?" Aunt Evelyn asked.

"How would I know?" Butch said.

"I noticed there were eight chicks instead of nine," Uncle Tyson said. "Then I saw a little mound in the straw."

"Didn't you tell me foxes get into the coop sometimes and kill chickens?" Butch remembered.

"Foxes eat them," Aunt Evelyn said. "They don't bury dead chicks in straw.

Butch went on eating, himself.

"Nothing to say?" Aunt Evelyn said.

Butch shook his head.

"You have no idea how this chick died?"

Again Butch shook his head.

Evelyn and Tyson looked at one another.

"I didn't expect this," Tyson said to her.

"It could be he really doesn't know," Evelyn said. "There could be another cause."

"Evelyn, please," Tyson said. "I know you like the boy."

"Benefit of the doubt," Evelyn said.

Uncle Tyson gave Butch a hard stare. "This time."

Butch was elated at how cleverly he'd tricked them. From now on, though, he must be careful. Because one thing was certain. He would do more killing.

He wanted to understand how God felt. No matter

how long it took.

Since it was obvious he couldn't kill the farm animals, he would kill other things. The fifty-acre farm had plenty of animals for him to practice on. There were birds galore. There were snakes and rats and a whole lot more.

He started right in.

He caught flies and tossed them into a spider's web and watched as the spider did what spiders do.

He discovered two kinds of ants, red and black, and saw that when they encountered one another, they fought fiercely. That gave him an idea. He located their nests, took an old tin cup, and gathered up a bunch of the reds. He then upended the cup over the nest of the blacks.

The mayhem it caused brought a grin and a laugh. Ants were savage fighters. They would pin one another and slash with their pincers and not relent until their adversary was dead.

Speaking of adversaries, he was witness to a spectacle the likes of which he never imagined.

On afternoon he heard a commotion near the orchard beyond the barn and ran to investigate.

The dominant rooster and a male pheasant were engaged in combat. Circling with their backs arched and their wings spread, they leaped and pecked and clawed. A lot of hens and a female pheasant were watching.

Butch's money was on the pheasant. It was bigger, and it was wild.

Yet the rooster won, triumphantly driving his foe off and then crowing proudly while parading in front of the hens.

One day Aunt Evelyn informed him that a lot of the meat they ate on the farm came from animals they killed. Pigs provided ham. Calves were carved into veal. Chickens were killed more often than the others.

Aunt Evelyn then asked Butch if he had any compunctions about killing.

Butch didn't know what compunctions were but he told her he could kill anything. He didn't add that in doing so he was being the same as God.

The next day she showed him how it was done.

First step, she caught a chicken. She explained that some were scooped up without a fuss but others had to be chased down.

She held the squirming hen under an arm, took hold of its neck, said, "Watch close. You have to give it a good wrench." And she did.

Butch liked the killing but not the plucking. It took forever to pull out all the feathers. The trick was to soak the chicken first so the feathers came out easier and you didn't get them up your nose and into your mouth.

He got so good at it, he could catch and kill and pluck a chicken in half the time it took Evelyn.

His next lesson in killing was one that stayed with him forever.

Fourteen cats lived on the farm. In the barn or in the outbuildings. None were house pets. Tyson and Evelyn kept them around to deal with all the mice and whatnot.

Tyson made a sport of it. He set out small wire traps in the barn that caught mice alive. Then he and the farm hands would place the trap in the center of the barnyard with a string tied to the latch that opened it. Tyson would ring a little bell and most of the cats would come and wait around the edge of the barnyard for him to pull on the string. The mouse would emerge and the cats would scramble to be the first to snatch it.

Tyson and the farm hands thought it was great fun and laughed heartily.

The farm couldn't support more than fourteen cats. Or so Aunt Evelyn informed Butch.

Now and then a female cat would have kittens, and to keep the number of cats down, Aunt Evelyn disposed of the excess.

She had Butch accompany her when she gathered up the latest batch of kittens---five----and put them in a cardboard box which she had him carry to the kitchen porch.

Taking an old milk pail, she asked Butch to work the pump handle to fill it. Then she put the pail between two chairs.

She sat in one and indicated that Butch should sit in the other.

"This is important," Aunt Evelyn said. "It's one of the most important of life's lessons you will ever learn."

Butch looked at the water in the pail and then at the cute little kittens moving about and mewing and trying to climb out of the cardboard box.

Aunt Evelyn picked up a kitten and placed it in her lap. Smiling, she stroked it and petted it. "There are times in life when we have to do things we may not want to do."

Butch waited expectantly.

"Watch close." Aunt Evelyn took the kitten by the

scruff of the neck, holding it much as the mother cat might do, and bending down, plunged it into the water clear down to the bottom of the pail---and held it there.

The water rippled and bubbled.

Aunt Evelyn went on holding the kitten down. "It's best to be sure." She waited a while longer and then raised the kitten out and set it on the cement. It lay limp and dripping. "Your turn. You do one now."

Butch reached into the box and petted one of the kittens, then cupped it in both hands and gently lifted it onto his lap. He petted it some more and it looked up at him with its innocent eyes and he petted it again and then gripped it by the scruff of its neck and pushed it into the pail of water, down to the bottom as Aunt Evelyn had done. He felt it thrash and went on holding it, as Aunt Evelyn had said to do. After a bit the thrashing stopped.

"That should be long enough," she said.

Butch raised the kitten out. It sagged in his grasp, dripping. He set it next to the first one.

"Want to do another?"

"Sure," Butch said. But not really. This wasn't like the baby chicken. He felt a sense of regret that life would make him do such a thing.

The farm was so different from Butch's normal life.

But that became different, too.

Every Saturday morning their mom picked them up and they spent Saturday and Sunday with her. Usually she would take them out to eat and shop and do fun things.

Saturday nights she would go out with a girlfriend and leave Butch to babysit his sister and brother.

Summer passed quickly. July came and went and August arrived, and with it, Bible School. Butch was bussed there and back. The classes were held in a church. During recess, he would make for the cemetery behind the church and prowl among the gravestones or walk along the top of the cemetery wall.

Butch made a friend, a boy named Terry. They would sit on the bus and talk. After a week Terry stopped coming and Butch kept to himself.

He liked the Bible Studies class . He took pride in memorizing the names of the Books of the Old and New Testaments

In late August an odd incident occurred. Butch was hiking in the woods with a neighbor, Jimmy. They were down at the creek, searching for crayfish and salamanders. Just as Butch bent to lift a rock at the water's edge there was a sort of whizzing *crack* and something struck a tree across the creek with a loud *thwack*. Barely a heartbeat after there came the blast of a rifle in the distance.

"What was that?" Jimmy blurted.

Butch's first thought was that someone was target shooting and that he and Jimmy had strayed into the line of fire. But there were no targets around except the trees and them.

The whizzing *crack* was repeated, this time inches from Butch's head.

Butch dived flat against a low bank. Jimmy was still standing and glancing all about in confusion. Quickly, Butch grabbed him by the arm and pulled him down beside him.

"What's going on?" Jimmy exclaimed.

"Someone is shooting at us."

"No way," Jimmy said. He started to raise his head and there was another *crack* and the distant shot.

"They're using a .22," Butch guessed by the sound.

"It must be someone playing a trick," Jimmy said. "Trying to scare us."

"Maybe so," Butch said. He could think of no other explanation. Still, "We'd better stay down a while."

They did. At last Butch warily pushed up high enough to see over the bank. No shots rang out. The woods were still.

"They stopped!" Jimmy said. "We can go now."

"Wait a bit more."

Butch let about ten minutes go by before he deemed it safe enough to slowly stand. He half expected another shot.

"That was weird," Jimmy declared.

Speaking of weird, about this time Butch decided that from now on, he would keep certain things to himself. With good reason.

His sister had taken to calling him 'weird'. At school many of the kids seemed to think he was more than a bit strange. Especially after he caught sight of a squirrel near where the buses parked. Without thinking, he snatched up a couple of rocks.

The squirrel was interested in an acorn and didn't notice Butch sneak up on it. His first stone caught it in the head. Blood spurted and the squirrel stumbled toward a tree. His second stone brought it down but the hit wasn't fatal and the squirrel was up again.

Butch glanced right and left for another rock and only then realized some of the girls were screaming and other kids were shouting and yelling for help.

A teacher's hand clamped onto his shoulder.

"My God, boy! What in the world got into you?"

Butch didn't answer.

He was ushered into the principal's office and endured over an hour of 'Why? Why? Why?'

The principal was kindly but troubled. As he put it, "No student of ours has ever tried to stone a squirrel to death before." He called Butch's mom and Butch had to wait until she arrived.

She was suprisingly calm. She told the principal that Butch spent a lot of time in the woods and on a farm and that he had a 'wild side'. She apologized for his behavior and promised an incident like this would never happen again.

The principal softened when she mentioned his dad dying. He said that he would let Butch off without punishment---this time---but nothing like it must ever happen again.

Butch's mother thanked him and smiled and placed her hand on Butch's shoulder and walked him out to her car. They were almost there when she dug her fingernails in and jerked him to a stop. Bending down, she looked him in the eyes.

"Don't you ever do anything like this to me again."

"To you?" Butch said.

"I was busy at something and I had to pull myself away to deal with it. Use your head, son. If you want to throw rocks at a squirrel, do it at home or in the woods. Not where everyone can see you."

"So you're not mad about me hurting the squirrel?"

His mom straightened. "Well, that too, of course."

There was another incident at school that winter. A rare ice storm sruck about midmorning. The principal came on the public address system to announce that all recesses would be held in the auditorium. Under no circumstances was anyone to venture outside. It was too dangerous.

During the afternoon recess, Butch and a couple of other boys found themselves near the EXIT door. Butch had never seen an ice storm and wanted to find out what the fuss was about. At an opportune moment, he and the other two slipped outside.

The playground was transformed. It had become a wonderland. Ice coated everything. The ground. The swing sets. The merry-go-round.

Butch discovered that if he took a few careful steps and then pushed off with one foot he could slide a considerable distance. It was like ice skating without ice skates. He and the others took to it with gusto, laughing and seeing who could slide the fartherest.

At one point, Butch slid close to a spot where part of the playground dipped into a lower area. Before he could stop himself, he slid over the brink and shot toward the teeter-totters. He was going so fast, he thought he might crash into them.

In order to slow down, as he zipped past the monkey bars he flung out his left arm to snag a bar. Instead, his forearm slipped between two of the bars and caught hold.

Butch's momentum was such that his feet swept into the air and his entire body arced upward. There was a loud snap and a sharp pain, and the next he knew, he was lying on his back and his wrist was hurting and his friends were bent over him asking if he was all right.

Butch said he felt okay but when he pulled up his shirt sleeve, he saw that something was wrong. It looked as if his wrist bone had snapped in half and part of one end was punching through his skin.

At luck would have it, at that moment Mrs. Carr started yelling at them from the top of the steps at the EXIT door. She demanded they come up immediately.

Butch quickly pulled his sleeve down and put his arm behind his leg.

"Did you see that?" Jake said.

"You need to tell the teacher," Craig urged.

"No," Butch said. "Keep quiet." He didn't want to get into trouble.

They filed to the steps where Mrs. Carr waited with her arms crossed and an angry expression on her face. "What were you three thinking? You heard the principal. No one is to be out here." She paused and her eyes narrowed. "Butch, why are you holding your arm that way?"

"What way?" Butch said.

"Behind your back like that. What is it? Did something happen?"

"I'm fine," Butch said.

"Let me see."

Reuluctantly, Butch brought his arm around and slowly pulled his sleeve up.

"Dear Lord!" Mrs. Carr exclaimed. "You broke your wrist!"

"I didn't mean to," Butch said.

"We need to get you to the school nurse right away.

Then we'll call your mother."

Butch expected the worst. He would be punished. Maybe banned from recess and his mom would make him do extra chores. But to his amazement he wasn't even scolded. The adults were so concerned about his wrist that not one of them thought to bring up his being out in the ice when he wasn't supposed to be.

Late in the summer of his tenth year Butch and his sister were playing tag in the cellar. They ran around and around the stairs, laughing and tagging each other. During one of their passes, his sister's flailing arm bumped his bamboo spear.

There was a story to the spear. A physician, Doc McClendon, lived up the lane from them. The doctor was considered the wealthiest in the neighborhood. He owned the most property. On it were large ponds that teemed with life, some of Butch's favorite haunts.

Doc McClendon had also created a rarity in that part of Pennsylvania. A bamboo forest. McClendon spent some of each summer in South America, in Brazil, treating the poor. Decades ago he brought several bamboo home and planted them. The result was a small 'forest', of an acre or so.

Butch loved it there. He would go and sit in the very middle so he was completely surrounded by the bamboo. On a still day, with the blue sky above, he experienced the most serene feeling, a sense of peace like nowhere else.

The bamboo fascinated him. He learned from Doc McClendon that bamboo was actually grass. That bamboo grew faster than most any other plant. When young, bamboo had a sheen to them that made Butch think of kitten fur. He liked to rub his hand up and down it. Older bamboo grew hard as rock.

Doc mentioned once that South American natives made spears out of bamboo. Butch asked how and Doc told him they would sharpen one end and hold it over a fire to harden it.

Butch wasted no time in duplicating their feat. He chopped a bamboo with his hatchet, sharpened it with his knife, and built a fire to harden the tip. It became his 'Frog Sticker', as he called it. He speared so many frogs and tadpoles, he lost count.

When not using it, he leaned it against the bottom of the cellar stairs.

So it was that Karen accidentally swung her arm against it when he was chasing her. The sharp end swung outward. The bottom end was wedged against a stair support beam.

Butch, laughing heartily, his mouth wide open, ran onto the spear. He had no time to react. It happened in a twinkling. The spear went into his mouth, the tip, as he would subsequently be told, shearing through the roof of his mouth into the bottom of his nose. The jolt lifted him off his feet. He fell onto his back, the spear jutting out. Without thinking he grabbed hold and pulled.

Blood gushed. Both out of his mouth and down his throat and out his nose.

Karen screamed and their mother came running.

His mom stopped and paled and then quickly recovered and dropped to her knees to slip a hand under his head. "Butch? Butch? Can you hear me?"

"He ran onto the spear!" Karen wailed.

Butch tried to speak but his mouth was filled with blood and all he could do was gurgle. He felt oddly calm. He kept swallowing blood.

His mom helped him up and hustled him out the cellar door to the car, barking at Karen to run upstairs and fetch a towel. Karen was back in no time, her eyes brimming but she kept control.

Butch pressed the towel to his mouth and bent his head so the blood seeped into it. The flow was much less. His mouth, oddly, didn't hurt all that bad. He slid into the back set and his mother ran inside for Mark and within two minutes they were streaking up the lane for the road that would take them to a hospital.

His mom kept asking was he woozy? Was he dizzy? Did he feel like he might pass out?

Butch tried to say that he was all right but all that came out was more gurgling and a glub.

At the hospital he was rushed into an emergency room and a doctor entered. Two nurses were on hand. The doctor used a little light to examine Butch's mouth, daubed at it with gauze, and requested tweezers.

Butch wondered what they were for and found out when the doctor carefully inserted them, gave a pull, and held up a large splinter for Butch to see.

"Can't leave that in there, can we?"

Butch laughed.

One of the nurses gave him a quizzical look.

The doctor went on examining and cleaning. At one point he made Butch open 'as wide as you can' and inserted a long needle-like instrument. Butch could feel him poking around and a strange sensation high in his mouth.

The doctor finally told a nurse to bring Butch's mom from the waiting room.

Butch lay quiet. His mouth didn't hurt much and he was no longer swallowing blood.

His mom entered holding Karen by the hand and clutching Mark to her chest. "How is he, Doctor Madison? Will he need to be admitted?"

"The bleeding has stopped. I'm afraid there's not much more that can be done."

The doctor went on to explain that the tip of the spear had pierced the top of Butch's mouth and gone clear through into the bottom of his nose. In effect, Butch now had an extra hole about the size of a nickel between his mouth and his nose.

"Can you sew it up?" his mom asked.

"Frankly, I don't see the need." The doctor informed them that the hole was so far back, he would have to clamp Butch's mouth open in order to ensure he didn't move while he was being operated on. It would require Butch to be put under and perhaps half an hour of surgery.

"Will the hole heal on its own?"

Dr. Madison regarded Buch thoughtfully. "The size it is? I doubt it. Oh, it will heal well enough. His mouth will be sore for a week or so and then he'll be good as new. But the hole itself will probably never close. He'll have it for as long as he lives."

"Will it cause problems for him?"

"I shouldn't think so."

Little did Butch know.

THE NOSE KNOWS

Butch's mouth slowly healed. And he discovered something no one anticipated.

His sense of smell and sense of taste were mixed in a way they weren't mixed before. Some people might say they were better.

Like when Aunt Evelyn baked an apple pie and offered him a slice fresh out of the oven. She'd set the plate in front of him and he would bend down and sniff to inhale the wonderful aroma. Then he would fork a piece into his mouth and close his mouth as he was supposed to, and chew. Before the new hole, with his mouth closed, he couldn't smell the piece he was eating.

Now he could.

The aroma wafted up through the hole in the roof of his mouth. He could smell what he was eating while he was eating it.

Not only that, if he smelled his food before he put it into his mouth, the fragrance went up his nose---and down the hole into his mouth.

He swore that he could taste it as well as smell it although he didn't understand how.

The new hole carried over into other things.

Flowers, for instance. Their scent was so much stronger. The same with his mom's perfume. She used so much that all he had to do was take a breath and he tasted the perfume on his tongue.

That aspect of his new hole wasn't so bad. But Butch soon discovered that every coin has its flip side, as the saying went.

For every pleasant smell, there are as many or more that aren't. Odors best avoided. Some so foul they made a person want to gag.

Butch felt that gag reflex a lot.

Before, he'd never given much thought to how people smelled. Now he did. Because to his chagrin, a lot of them---a very awful lot---didn't smell all that good. Dried sweat was the most common odor they gave off. A lot---a surprising lot---had a stink about them.

Later in life he found out that how they smelled was a reliable indicator of their state of health.

Or how they tasted.

It was strange but some people had a natural sweet scent. Others, not so much.

And it wasn't just people. No two dogs or cats or cows smelled the same.

Then there were dog droppings and the cat's litter box. Or when someone farted. A thousand and one reeks that caused him to start breathing as shallow as he could in order not to want to heave.

He didn't tell anyone what the hole had done. His own sister and a lot of the kids already regarded him as strange. Why give them cause to think him even stranger?

In other regards life went on pretty much as before. There was school. There was the woods. There was TV. He especially liked to watch shows he'd watched with his dad. The boxing matches. The wrestling. *Peter Gunn. The Rifleman.*

A new show came on, one Butch liked a lot. It was called *The Tall Man* and was about Billy the Kid. He would sit with his face glued to the TV screen and wish he was as cool as Billy.

Then his mother announced that she wanted him to start taking dancing lessons.

Butch was shocked. He didn't want to dance. But his mom said that a man should learn so that when he was out with a lady he could show her a good time.

And the dancing lessons, it turned out, were on the same night as *The Tall Man.* To Butch's heartfelt dismay, he had to give up watching his favorite show.

Instead, his mom dressed him in a too-tight fancy suit with polished shoes and drove him to the studio where he and mostly a lot older kids were taught how to waltz and tango and other dances.

He wasn't very good at them. He'd hold himself as stiff as a board and keep repeating "1, 2, 3, 1, 2, 3," in his head in time to the steps he was supposed to take.

He asked his mom if he could stop going. She shook her head. He begged her. To no avail.

In desperation he prayed to God.

Saturday evening came around and they were on their way yet again. Butch was in the back seat, thinking how God had let him down.

They were on Germantown Pike, heading south, and came to construction. His mother braked behind another car to wait until a man with a STOP sign would let them continue.

A minute went by and she glanced in the rearview

mirror and suddenly screamed, "Look out!"

The words were barely out of her mouth when several things happened simultaneously.

There was a tremendous sound, a grinding roar, and the rear part of the roof buckled, smashing down onto Butch's head and nearly pinning him to the seat.

Karen screamed.

Mark cried out.

At the same instant the station wagon was violently propelled forward and spun partway and crashed into the car in front of them.

Butch was stunned. He realized his head was bleeding and the blood was getting into his eyes. He tried to move but something was pressing him down.

He could see his sister huddled against the far door, crying.

His mother was yelling.

A great commotion broke out. Other people were shouting, too.

Butch managed to twist his head enough to look out his window. It was shattered. A lot of men and women were around their station wagon and a man with dark hair peered in and said urgently but kindly, "Don't move, son! We'll get you out as soon as we can!" He paused. "How bad are you?"

"I don't know," Butch said. "What happened?"

"You were hit."

Butch wanted to know more but the man moved away. He saw the far door wrenched open and Karen was lifted out. He heard his mother somewhere outside the station wagon. She sounded scared.

Red lights were flashing.

Butch could smell the seat cushion under him. He also smelled the strong odor of gas.

The roof had buckled so that he couldn't sit up. He was forced to stay bent over the seat.

He wanted out.

It seemed to take forever. Eventually there were peculiar sounds, as of metal being rent.

Gentle hands pulled him clear.

The police were there, and a fire truck and an ambulance.

A man in a white uniform examined him and announced that he should be taken to a hospital.

While he was being examined, Butch took the whole scene in and listened to what was being said.

A dump truck had crashed into their station wagon. A huge thing that dwarfed their vehicle. The driver was being questioned by several police officers. One of them mentioned something called a sobriety test.

His mother and sister and brother were all right. Apparently, he was the only one hurt.

A miracle it wasn't worse, someone commented.

Butch endured the ride to the hospital in silence. All he could think of was that he had missed *The Tall Man* yet again.

At the hosptial emergency room a doctor announced he would need stitches but otherwise he appeared to be fine.

"This might hurt," the doctor said as he applied them.

Butch felt a prickling sensation and tiny sharp points of pain. A strong antiseptic smell pervaded the air. It was rather pleasant.

Afterward, the doctor told him that once the stitches were removed, Butch would have a scar. It made Butch smile. He would be just like his dad.

Since the station wagon would take a lot of money to repair, his mother decided that, instead, she would buy a new car. One for her, as she put it. She used some of the insurance money from their dad's death and purchased a brand new *Ford Fairlane* bright purple convertible with a white top.

She loved it. She said as much again and again.

She also bought new clothes for herself. The long dresses she wore when their dad was alive were stored in a trunk. Now she wore short skirts and bright tops and went around in a leopard skin coat that she loved almost as much as her convertible.

Butch considered her a whole new mom. He and his sister were puzzled when she started to drink a lot. Her favorite was whiskey. Nearly every evening she would open a big bottle and sit at the kitchen table by herself and drink glass after glass.

Another change was that on Friday or Saturday night or both she would dress up and go out with a girlfriend to a bar, leaving Butch to watch over things.

He didn't know what to think when she started bringing men home. Whoever she brought would spend the night in her bedroom.

All the men, Butch learned, were truck drivers.

There were four of them. At first it was never the same man twice. They rotated, apparently because they were in town at different times.

Then she seemed to take a liking to one in particular and he came a lot.

Butch liked him. He was the nicest of the bunch. Another was big and friendly and always smelled of the *Brylcreem* he used to slick his hair. Butch sensed hostility from the third and the fourth treated him and his sister and brother as if they didn't exist.

The sounds they made when they were with his mom varied from man to man.

Before all this, Butch's mother had finished off the upstairs by adding two bedrooms. On the north side was his sister's. On the south, a bedroom for Butch and his little brother.

Which happned to be directly above his mother's.

So it was that on nights she brought the truck drivers home, Butch had to lay and listen to the many sounds coming from below. Rustlings and creakings and grunts and moans, and more.

When the big, friendly man was over, there were loud thuds that went on forever, as if his mom's bed were jumping up and down.

When the nicest man was there, Butch would hear his mother moaning *Gene! Gene! Oh Gene!* over and over and over.

It kept him up to all hours.

He didn't say anything to his mom. He had heard her say more than once that she was very lonely since their dad died. He figured being with the truck drivers made her feel less alone.

He underwent a change of his own. Ever since he was born, he would have what his mom called his 'sickly bouts'. He would grow pale and pasty and feel weak. Sometimes it only lasted a few hours. Other times, two or three days. He would also, now and then, vomit.

Those bouts became more frequent.

His mother took him to Dr. Watson several times to find out what was wrong. The physician was stumped. Watson ran test after test and finally admitted to Butch's mom that he had no idea what was causing the bouts.

A new summer was upon them when another mishap occurred.

This time Karen was involved. She was running toward the outside cellar door when she tripped and went through it head-first. The glass shattered into a thousand shards. Yet somehow she escaped with only a few cuts.

In the woods and on the farm Butch continued to kill. Anything and everything he came across. Snakes, birds, frogs, you name it.

It was the best excitement he knew.

One day Aunt Evelyn and Uncle Tyson were enjoying the evening air in their rockers on the farmhouse porch when Tyson pointed off across a field and said, "Look at that, will you? In our corn again."

A dark animal about the size of a small dog was moving along the fringe of the newly grown corn.

"What is it?" Butch asked.

"A groundhog," Aunt Evelyn said. "Some call them woodchucks. We have quite a few."

"They cause a lot of damage," Uncle Tyson said.

"Kill them," Butch suggested.

Aunt Evelyn sighed. "They mainly come out in the early morning and about the time we eat supper. I'm too busy then."

"I used to shoot them when I could," Tyson said.

"I have too much work these days.

"Let me," Butch said, delighted at the prospect. He had become quite the shot with their .22 rifle.

"If you want," Evelyn said. "Don't get too close to them," she cautioned. "They grow to about two feet tall and can weigh upwards of fifteen pounds." She added, "And they have big teeth."

Butch took to the task with relish.

From his *Golden Nature Guide to MAMMALS*---one of several guides which were part of his growing library---he learned that groundhogs lived in burrows. To kill them, all he had to do was stake out the holes they used to enter and leave, and when one emerged, pick it off with the rifle.

But shooting them soon lost is luster.

It was too easy. He could lie hidden fifty yards away, and *bang*, the job was done. He prided himself on always needing only one shot. To the head. He didn't see any sense to making them suffer. Which in itself was a new outlook.

Since it wasn't much fun using the .22, Butch decided to to change tactics. Instead of the gun he needed something else. But what? He could use his uncle's pitchfork but his uncle might need it for forking hay and straw and would notice it was missing.

A knife would be too short and take a lot of stabbing.

An unlikely source gave him the answer. He was immensely fond of the *My Bookhouse* series edited by Olive Beaupre Miller. He had read and reread them again and again.

The fourth, *The Treasure Chest*, was his favorite.

It contained a story about Hercules, a strongman of long ago who wore a lion skin and used a club.

Why not do the same?

Butch searched the orchard and the cherry tree plot and the woods and found a suitably thick and stout piece of a branch that fit his ideal of a club. He practiced swinging it and hefting it and when he was ready, put his plan into effect.

First, he chose the groundhog, a large male that came out every morning and evening to feed on new corn shoots. The opening to its den was on a slight rise. Past the rise was a short slope. It was there that Butch hid. He had on shorts and a T-shirt and sneakers. Cradling his club, he huddled perfectly still until a grunting sound alerted him that the male groundhog had emerged from its burrow.

Butch let a little time go by before he raised up high enough to peer over the rise.

The groundhog was in among the new shoots, eating, oblivious to his presence.

Butch slowly stood and just as slowly stepped over the rise and past the burrow, placing himself between the hole and the groundhog. He didn't say anything or make any noise. He simply waited, the tapered end of the club in his right hand, the thick end resting on the ground.

This particular groundhog was as big and fat as a groundhog could be. It went on eating until at one point it stood on its hind legs and gazed off toward the distant farmhouse and let out a low whistle. Then it resumed filling its belly.

Butch decided the time had come. "Hey there," he

said.

Barking in surprise, the groundhog spun and jerked upright. It stood nearly as high as Butch's knees. It let out a long hiss.

Butch firmly gripped his club in both hands and crouched.

Uttering a gutteral growl, the groundhog bared its long incisors.

Butch waited.

The groundhog growled louder and dropped onto all fours.

Still Butch waited.

The groundhog glanced at the entrace to its burrow and then at Butch and came at him in a rush. It leaped high, at Butch's thigh, even as Butch swung with all his might. His club caught it on the shoulder and it fell but immediately scrambled to its feet and leaped again, its incisors wide to rend. Butch arced his club and sent the groundhog tumbling. Furious at being thwarted, it was up and at him in a twinkling. Butch pivoted, swung, struck. The groundhog sprang at his ankle. He arced the club and caught it on the top of its skull. Falling flat, the groundhog hissed and snarled and sought to rise. Butch smashed his club down again and again and again and again. Finally he stopped, out of breath, his entire body vibrant with pure excitement.

The groundhog's skull was partially caved in, its blood and brains seeping out.

Butch raised his face and his club to the heavens and let out with a Tarzan yell like he had seen the apeman do in movies on TV. His cry rang loud and clear and for a few moments he felt as if he were more alive than he had ever been.

This wasn't like killing frogs or birds.

This had been a fair fight.

Him and his club against the groundhog with its teeth and claws.

And he had won!

He stared at the dead groundhog with its oozing brains and at his club marked red with the groundhog's blood and he looked skyward again and laughed.

This was how life should be!

Picking the groundhog up by a rear leg, he tossed it into high weeds that bordered the corn. Then, the club over his shoulder, he strolled toward the farmhouse, savoring the feeling of being so acutely alive.

He held out the club and smiled. He'd never felt this way when he shot a groundhog. That was too easy. There was no challenge. There was no danger to him.

On equal footing, equal terms, the experience was delicious.

Yes, that was how he would describe it. Delicious.

He had other delicious experiences.

Like the time he jumped off the loft in the barn into a giant mound of straw. He turned as he dropped, spreading his arms and legs, and came down on his back with hardly a jolt. He smiled at how much fun it was and was rising to do it again when he noticed a pitchfork lying not an arm's length away. A little closer and he would have landed on the tines and impaled himself. He laughed at his close call.

Another time he was exploring a creek near the farm when he came around a bend. A wide pool proved tempting. It was a hot day. He was only wearing shorts and sandles and he waded in. The water rose as high as his ankles and then his knees.

Butch became aware of a strange sensation, as of a lot of little fingers rubbing against his skin. He looked down and realized there were over a dozen thin wriggling creatures swirling about his legs. At first he took them for worms but he couldn't fathom why worms were in the water like that.

Then it hit them.

They weren't worms. They were snakes. Not just any snake. They were a kind he rarely came across. Their markings and their yellow tails made that plain. And they were venomous.

They were water moccasins.

Or as some people called them, cottonmouths.

Butch froze. He'd heard accounts of people who were bitten by water moccasins. Some recovered. Some didn't. Supposedly the young weren't as poisonous as a grown adult but they were able to inflict a venomous bite.

If he moved he might rile them and be bitten more than once. In which case all that poison would pump through his veins.

The young snakes went on brushing against him as if his legs were downed tree limbs they were playing around.

With a start it occurred to him that their mother might be somewhere near. Firming his grip on his club, he glanced right and left. He didn't know if snakes were as protective of their young as, say, bears.

His nerves ate at him. The longer he stood there,

the more likely he might be bitten.

Making a sudden decision, Butch bolted for the bank. Moving as fast as the water allowed he reached dry ground and clambered out.

Quickly, he inspected both legs, expecting to find bite marks. There were none.

Butch looked at the pool and laughed.

Yet another close call involved another type of snake, a black racer.

The woods that hemmed his neighborhood on three sides extended for miles. Off to the west, they ended at an old quarry near a hospital. The hospital used it as a dump. A pond at the bottom was fouled with the things that were tossed in. The water even turned green.

A cliff bordered the pond, a narrow ledge running from top to the bottom.

Butch was descending one day, his gaze on the pond, when a black racer that was apparently sunning itself on the ledge did what black racers were notorious for doing. It coiled and struck. They liked to bite, the racers. They weren't poisonous, but still.

Butch reacted without thinking. He threw himself back and to one side. The snake missed and shot past him up the ledge.

In his haste, though, Butch stepped off into empty space---and he was a good sixty feet up. Frantic, he managed to catch hold of clumps of long-stemmed grass to keep from falling. Bracing himself against the cliff, he was able to pull himself onto the ledge.

The black racer was gone.

Butch lay on his back and gazed at the sky and

laughed.

Often, Butch went shopping with Aunt Evelyn. He liked stores. He liked toys. Once, he talked her into buying him a *Ramar Of the Jungle* playset complete with animals and trees and everything. The brown gorilla was one of his favorites.

On an early morning one summer's day they went to an *ACME*. Near the cash registers was a rack, a spinner, filled with comic books.

Butch made a beeline for it, eager to find a *Tarzan* or maybe a *Turok, Son Of Stone* or *Green Lantern*. Instead he found something completely new. *Amazing Spider-Man #5*.

Butch asked Aunt Evelyn to buy it but she refused. She wasn't fond of frivolous things, as she called them, and in her estimation comic books were as frivolous as they came. Butch persisted, saying "Please!" a lot, and at last she relented.

Butch was so excited, he read it on the way home. He loved Spider-Man's costume and the story. He loved how Spider-Man shot webbing and clung to things.

He helped Aunt Evelyn take the groceries in and then went upstairs and and read it again. He wished more than anything that he could do what Spider-Man did.

He happened to glance out his bedroom door and saw his aunt's sewing machine in the hall. It was a big, old-fashioned thing. She had to pump with her feet to make it work. On it was a large spool pin for holding thread and whatnot. And on the spool pin was a roll of thread.

Inspiration struck.

Scrambling off the bed, Butch hurried over and slid the roll off the pin. He had seen her do it many times. The thread was pink, the roll big enough that he could hold it in the palm of his hand and pretend it was Spider-Man's web shooter.

Where to use it?

Again inspiraton struck.

Butch darted upstairs to the third floor. It was seldom used since there were enough bedrooms on the second.

The front window of an unused bedroom opened onto an extended overhang that ran the entire width of the second story. Undoing the latch, he slid the window up and climbed out. Shingles crunched under his feet.

The overhang sloped so he had to be careful as he moved to the rain spout at the corner.

Butch looked down. It wasn't more than twenty-five feet. Eagerly, he tied the end of the thread to the junction of the spout and gutter by sliding the thread under and looping it several times.

Now, when he held the spool in the palm of his hand, he could let it out between his first and second finger, much as Spider-Man did with his webbing.

Giddy at this new thrill, Butch eased onto the spout. He held fast with his other hand and clamped his legs to the gutter. Now he could slide down while letting his 'web shooter' play out.

The instant he started down something went wrong. His body went faster than he anticipated and he lost his grip. He felt himself start to fall and in desperation clutched the spool tighter, thinking it might slow him a little.

It didn't.

As his great aunt later imparted, she was in the parlor enjoying her daily soap opera when she heard a loud squawk and glanced out the parlor window in time to see Butch go plummeting past. She also thought she heard the thud of him hitting the ground.

Butch was dazed. And aching all over. He lay staring up at the rain spout and started to laugh when his vision was filled by an aged, somber face.

"What on earth?" Aunt Evelyn said.

"Hi," Butch said.

"What did you think you were doing?"

"Being Spider-Man."

"Being what?"

Butch held out the spool of pink thread. She took it and he pointed at the spot on the third floor where he had tied it and explained about the comic book with Spider-Man and about using the spool as a web-shooter but it hadn't worked.

Aunt Evelyn looked at the thread and up at the rain spout and down at Butch. "My word."

"Sorry I broke your thread," Butch thought to say.

"I never heard the like," Aunt Evelyn declared. "Who in their right mind would do such a thing?"

"I can put it back on the sewing machine for you," Butch offered.

Aunt Evelyn bent her considerable bulk until her face was inches from his. "I am never buying you another of those comic book things for as long as I live."

She walked off.

"Well, darn," Butch said.

One more incident took place late in the summer. Butch was invited to spend the weekend with a new friend, Derek. Derek wanted to go exploring along Perkiomen Creek, which was a mile or more from his house. Derek's mom drove them there and told them she would return to pick them up at the same spot in two hours.

For the first hour Butch had great fun. They roved the bank and spotted all kinds of wildlife, including a large snapping turtle. Butch was so invested in the wonders of Nature that he was puzzled when Derek nudged him hard and pointed.

"What's that guy up to?"

Butch looked.

A big black car was driving past on the road adjacent to the creek.

For some reason the word *Cadillac* popped into Butch's head.

"That's the third time he's gone past," Derek said.

"Probably looking for a fishing spot," Butch imagined. There were lots of pull-over areas---basically patches of dirt---for that very purpose.

"I don't like it," Derek said. "My mom says we have to watch out."

This was new to Butch. "For what?"

"Sometimes they take kids."

Butch started to laugh but caught himself. "Wait. You're serious?"

"Look. Here he comes again."

Sure enough, the big black car was coming back along the road. This time it didn't go past. The driver pulled into a dirt area nearby and got out.

"What's he up to?" Derek said suspiciously.

Butch couldn't help but think his friend was making a big deal over nothing.

The man---large and burly with a huge gut---didn't even glance in their direction. He went around to the rear of the *Cadillac* and opened the trunk.

"See?" Butch said. "He's going to go fishing."

But no. The man stepped to the side and looked directly at them and smiled. "Hi there, boys."

"Hi!" Butch called out, smiling.

"Don't talk to him," Derek said.

"Want to see some fish I caught?" the man yelled. "They're big ones!"

"Want to?" Butch said.

"Are you nuts?" Derek said. He bent toward Butch and spoke in a whisper even though they were too far from the man for him to hear them. "Do exactly as I do. When I tell you to, run."

"Run?" Butch said.

Derek snagged his wrist and pulled him along and they moved in the general direction of the *Cadillac* but not straight for it. Instead, Derek angled toward the edge of the road.

"Yes sir!" the man was saying. "A bass this big!" He held his hands well apart.

"He's just being friendly," Butch said.

"Do you see a fishing pole?" Derek angrily replied. He shook his head in annoyance. "I had no idea you were so dumb."

They were almost to the road.

"What are you doing?" the man hollered. "You're moving away."

"Run!" Derek said, and did, again pulling Butch with him.

Butch ran. When he glanced back he saw that the man had shut the trunk and was hurrying to the front door. The man slid in and the car began to execute a wide turn.

"This way!" Derek said, and darted into the woods bordering the creek.

The growth was thick. Branches and brambles tore at Butch's face and clothes. He was embarrassed at what they were doing but Derek was so serious about it that he went along anyway.

Derek cut to the right, staying in the woods, and Butch followed suit.

Without warning Derek stopped so abruptly that Butch ran into him.

"Down!" Derek said, grabbing him and yanking him low.

Off through the trees the black car was moving slowly past. The man's face was framed in the open window.

"He's searching for us," Derek said.

"Probably wants to know why we ran away," Butch said.

Twice more the car went by and then they heard it pick up speed and move off toward Germantown Pike.

"We're safe now," Derek said. "We'll lay low until it's time to meet up with my mom."

"I don't think we were in any real danger," Butch mentioned.

Derek's mom disagreed. At her insistence, Derek's dad called the police who came out and questioned

Derek and Butch at length.

When Butch's mom arrived to pick him up, Derek shook Butch's hand in parting.

"I'm never having you over again."

Derek was true to his word.

IF AT FIRST YOU DON'T SUCCEED

Despite his aunt Butch wasn't deterred. He immersed himself in superheroes. He had been reading DC comics for a while now---*Green Lantern, The Flash, Superman* and others----his favorite was *Adam Strange* in *Mystery In Space*.

Presently he discovered that the company which published *Spider-Man* put out a great many more. *The Fantastic Four, Strange Tales, Tales Of Suspense, Tales to Astonish, The Avengers, The X-Men*. He couldn't get enough. He spent every penny of his allowance on comics. He spent every minute he could reading them.

And making them real.

He took an old metal trash lid and beat the rim flat with a hammer so he could have a shield like Captain America's. He asked his mom for a bow from SEARS for Christmas so he could be like Hawkeye. He even modified his arrows. Hawkeye used exploding arrows so Butch tied firecrackers or M-80's to his arrows and lit them and let fly to have exploding arrows of his own.

He dreamed constantly about how wonderful it would be to live as a superhero. To go around helping people and battling supervillains.

One day a startling thought occurred to him. Why not? So far as he was aware there weren't any real superheroes. But again, why not? All you needed was a costume to hide your secret identity and a weapon to battle the evildoers, and presto, you were a superhero.

The more Butch pondered, the more the idea appealed to him.

He would become the world's first real superhero!

But what to call himself?

Yet another comic inspired him. Not *Marvel* or *DC*. Put out by Gold Key, it was about a superhero called *The Phantom*. The name appealed to him. It denoted an air of mystery.

Now he needed a costume. Unfortunately, he wasn't aware of a single store that sold superhero costumes. He would have to make his own. Since he wasn't much good at sewing, and he couldn't very well ask his mom to buy a purple shirt and pants and boots without her wanting to know why, he'd have to make do with clothes he already owned.

He tried on different shirts and pants and studied himself in his bedroom mirror. None were 'superhero' enough.

Then one morning he was standing in front of the mirror in his T-shirt and underwear---and did a double-take. They matched, since both were white. And they weren't all that different from the spandex superheroes wore. He tucked the T-shirt into his underwear and gnawed his lip.

Something was missing.

Going to his dresser, he took out a black *Magic Marker*. He took the T-shirt off, spread it out on the floor, and proceeded to draw a large skull on the chest with *The Phantom* in large bold letters above it. Quickly, he slipped into the shirt again and admired his handiwork.

Perfect! he complimented himself, and turned his attention to his feet. He tried sneakers but they looked dumb. His dress shoes for Sunday School were even dumber. He took them off and regarded himself in his socks.

They were perfect in that they were white and matched the rest. Except he couldn't very well go running around outdoors with only socks on.

Rocks and whatnot would poke the heck out of his feet.

Racking his brain, Butch dressed and hurried down to the cellar. In a corner were cardboard boxes his mom stored stuff in. He chose the box with the thickest cardboard. It was a simple matter to cut off a couple of the flaps and hurry back up to his bedroom. He set the pieces of cardboard on the floor and placed his right foot on one and his left on the other. Then, using the *Magic Marker*, he traced the outline of each foot. Carefully cutting with scissors, he soon had improvised soles he slid into each sock.

Now he need not worry about being poked and pricked.

Next was the biggie. A mask. He toyed with the notion of making one like *Zorro*'s or *The Lone Ranger*'s but they would leave too much of his face exposed. Plus, he couldn't very well tie the mask over his horn-rimmed glasses. It would look downright stupid. Even if he put the mask on under them.

Thwarted, it was a week or so before a solution presented itself.

He happened to be at the farm. One day he went

up to his bedroom while his Aunt Evelyn was watching her soap opera. He glanced into her and Tyson's bedroom and spied a pair of her nylon stockings draped over an open drawer. It was rare for her to leave them out like that.

Curious, he listened to be sure she was enrapt in her show, then went over.

He was familiar with his mom's stockings. Thin, sheer, light things.

These were heavy and thick, so thick you couldn't see through them like you could his mom's. The top part resembled his underpants.

He was kneading the fabric with his fingers when a brainstorm struck.

The nylon stretched and would be easy to cut.

When his mom came to pick them up that evening, Butch smuggled his great aunt's stockings out in the overnight bag that contained his pajamas and spare shirt and toothbrush.

He kept expecting Aunt Evelyn to phone and ask his mom if she knew what had happened to her nylons but she never did.

Alone in the privacy of his room, Butch set to work. He cut off one of the legs. It was much too long so he snipped it off below the knee. By experimenting, he found that he could pull the underpants part on over his head. The bottom came to below his chin. The top, though, flopped about like a limp towel. He solved that by tying a big knot.

Due to how thick the nylon was, he couldn't see his hand at arm's length. He solved that problem by cutting holes and stretching the nylon around his glasses.

The mirror confirmed that he looked positively spectacular.

All that was left now was to pick a weapon. He considered the trash can shield and his bow but opted instead for his pair of bone-handled hunting knives. One on each hip.

Butch couldn't wait to go into action. He bubbled with excitement at the prospect. But how and where to go about it?

They lived out in the country, in a rural area where there wasn't hardly ever any crime. There were no banks for criminals to rob, no jeweler's to be broken into.

The next morning he had another brainstorm.

Butch went down to fetch the milk bottles out of the milkbox by the cellar door. It gave him cause to think about the milk truck that delivered the milk several times a week, and how his mom often left an envelope in the milkbox with money to pay the bill and a little extra besides.

Other people did the same.

Which meant that the milk trucks were easy prey for anyone who wanted to rob them. He'd never heard of a milk truck being robbed but there was always a first time for everything. Sooner or later a robber was bound to think of it.

Butch laughed in delight. He would protect milk trucks!

There was a hitch, though. Milk trucks came around early in the morning. Really early, like six a.m. To protect them, he'd need to get up even earlier so he could be on patrol when the trucks made their rounds.

No problem. He had an alarm clock.

Time to be a superhero!

The very next morning Butch put his dream into effect. He was up at five. His brother stirred but didn't wake up.

Donning his costume, Butch snuck downstairs. He quietly slipped out the back door and made his way up the lane to Trooper Road. Somewhere a rooster crowed as Butch ran along behind the houses that lined Trooper Road. There weren't that many. After he passed the last, he cut across to the other side where there were a few more and eventually came to Woodland Avenue.

He didn't see a single milk truck. For that matter, he didn't see any cars or trucks at all.

Ducking behind a pine stree, his hands on the hilts of his knives, Butch waited. Superheroes needed to be patient.

Half an hour went by and no milk trucks appeared.

Butch needed to get home. His mom would be up soon. He cut across back yards again and hastened down the lane and was safe in his bedroom before anyone woke up.

Congratulating himself on a job well done on his first patrol, Butch committed another act of daring. He wore his costume under his school clothes. He ate breakfast as usual and the bus came as usual and he took a seat at the back as he usually did.

Then something unusual happened.

A girl named Sandy Wood lived along Trooper Road. In fact, she lived in the last house, the one Butch had cut across twice while on patrol. Lustrous black hair fell to her waist, and she had the prettiest eyes.

Normally, Sandy sat with other girls toward the front of the bus. Today she climbed on and stopped and stared at him and then came down the aisle and sat in the seat in front of him, turning so they faced each other.

"Hi Butch."

"Sandy," Butch greeted her, puzzled. She hardly ever spoke to him.

"How are you?" Sandy asked.

"Fine," Butch said. "You?"

"I want to ask you a question. Actually, my mom wants me to ask you."

"Your mom?"

"Were you up near our house earlier?"

Unease spiked through Butch. "Why would I do that?" he hedged.

"She thinks she saw you."

"Huh?" Butch said, his unease becoming mild panic.

"She gets up early. Today she went out to the kitchen and was at the sink filling a glass when she looked out the window and saw someone running across our back yard."

"It could have been anyone."

"My mom says it was a boy your size."

"There are lots of boys my size."

"Skinny like you, too."

Butch's mouth had gone dry. "Lots of skinny kids around."

"She says you were in your underwear."

Butch forced a laugh. "Why would anybody be

running around outside in their underwear?"

"She couldn't be sure but she also thinks you were wearing a nylon on your head with a great big knot on top. It kind of shocked her. She said she couldn't believe what she was seeing."

"So she couldn't see the face of whoever it was?" Butch said, his spirits rising.

"No," Sandy said. "But she could see their glasses sticking out through the nylons. She says their glasses were just like yours."

"A lot of kids have glasses like mine."

"She says to tell you to never, ever do that again. If she sees you again, she'll tell your mother."

"It wasn't me," Butch lied.

Sandy stood. "I've always known you were weird. I just never realized how weird." She made for the front of the bus. Joining her friends, she huddled close and they listened to her and kept glancing back at him and then all of them burst out laughing.

Butch sat straight and smiled, wishing he could wither into his seat.

From now on he must be more careful. And he must find something else to protect besides milk trucks.

For days he was at a loss. Until he caught a newcast on the radio about how poachers were killing a lot of animals for their hides and the meat.

Poachers. Butch had heard tell they also drove back roads late at night and shined flashlights on deer and shot them.

But Butch couldn't very well go out on patrol after dark. His mom made him go to bed at ten.

What animal could he protect that didn't involve

going out at night?

The answer was obvious.

Muskrats.

In the woods near their house was a creek that ran year-round. It contained fish and and salamanders and crayfish. It was also home to muskrats.

Butch knew all about them. In fact, he'd once trapped them for their fur. He'd talked his mom into buying half a dozen traps and every day during trapping season he made the rounds of those he'd set, killed any muskrats he caught, skinned them, cured the hide, and sold the skins to a dealer. He got .75 for an average pelt, up to $1.25 if it was prime, which they rarely were.

He'd only trapped for a season. His allowance was seventy-five cents a month so he was glad to have the extra money. But an incident soured him on it.

Muskrat traps didn't have teeth, like some traps. The whole point was to avoid damaging their fur. To that end, Butch used what were called coil-spring foothold traps. To set one, he placed it on the ground, pressed his feet onto the long spring with enough force to lower the jaws, then carefully fit the dog into the notch on the pan lever.

Traps had to be set just right, at the most likely point to catch the muskrat as it was leaving or entering its den.

One day he decided to use a trap to catch something other than a muskrat. He'd been told that he could get good money for rabbit fur. It had to be cured just right and the fur kept soft and pliable.

To that end, Butch went into deep brush bordering the woods and located a number of rabbits runs.

Tunnels, sort of, that rabbits and other animals used to travel about.

He set a trap in a run and covered it with leaves.

The very next day it had caught something. But not a rabbit.

Butch was astounded to find a pheasant foot in the trap. Evidentaly the bird had been using the run to go about under cover and stepped in the trap. In its frantic attempts to get free, it tore its foot off.

Butch opted to keep the foot as a keepsake, and reset the trap. When he got home, he cut a strip of rawhide and made a necklace out of the foot. But no sooner did he proudly show it to his mom than she told him she never wanted to see him wearing it again.

"I don't want that disgusting thing anywhere near me," were her exact words.

A few days later Butch went back to check the rabbit trap. He parted the brush and extended his hand down and in his haste, he carelessly pressed his thumb againt the pan.

There was a metallic *snap* and pain shot up his arm clear to his shoulder.

The trap had closed on his thumb! His first thought was that it might be broken. In panicked reflex he pulled on the trap---and couldn't budge it. When he'd initially placed it, he'd pounded a stake at the end of its chain deep into the ground so that whatever it caught couldn't get away.

But now he was the one caught. The trap had him fast.

His pain grew worse by the moment.

Butch gripped the trap with his other hand, braced

himself, and strained. The trap moved an inch or so, nowhere near enough for him to depress the spring and release his thumb.

He could feel the jaws biting into his flesh, feel wet drops dribbling down his thumb.

Butch willed himself to stay calm. The jaws weren't sharp enough to tear his thumb off. Then again, what if the bone was shattered?

His hand grew wetter. He couldn't tell how badly he was bleeding but it wasn't a good sign.

Butch tried to get a solid grip on the chain with his other hand. He couldn't quite manage it.

He was stuck, trapped as surely as a muskrat would have been. Or a rabbit. Or that pheasant.

Strange to relate, at that moment an overwhelming insight gripped him, an insight he'd never had before

This was no way for something to die.

To be caught, helpless, until the trapper came along to bash in their brains or shoot them.

Butch had never looked at it from the muskrat's point of view before.

Growing frantic, he dug in his feet. He refused to give up. This was entirely on him. There was no one around who could help. He could shout himself hoarse and it was unlikely anyone would hear.

And who knew what might come along while he was caught fast? A bear, maybe.

His body broke out in sweat. He felt clammy all over.

Setting himself, he tried again and again and again. Each attempt left him spent and in more pain.

Overhead, the sun slowly climbed.

Butch was thirsty enough to drink their well dry.

No one knew he was in the woods. His mom was at work. He wouldn't be missed until she got home, hours away.

For the umpteenth time Butch strained for all he could muster. For the umpteenth time he slumped in defeat. He was becoming weaker. He envisioned night descending and having to endure all those hours of darkness with predators abroad.

Butch bowed his head and closed his eyes. It had been a while since he prayed. A long while.

He prayed now. Prayed fervently. Glancing skyward, he was relieved that the Three Stooges didn't appear.

His hand felt numb.

Butch twisted and pulled and almost whooped for joy when his thumb gave a little. Not much, but he could wriggle it.

In doing so, he felt the jaws of the trap grate on bone.

It was the incentive he needed.

In burst of renewed energy, Butch twisted and turned and pulled and yanked and his thumb began to ever-so-slowly slide free. Maybe the blood made it slick. Whatever the cause, he gave a titanic backward lunge and the next he knew he was on his back free of the trap and his hand, parts of it smeared red, was in front of his face.

The thumb didn't appear to be broken. He could move it, although doing so hurt a lot.

Right then and there Butch made a decision. He wasn't going to trap anymore.

So perhaps it was only natural that when he cast about for a new task to set for himself in his role as a superhero, he hit on the notion of protecting muskrats from poachers.

The very next afternoon he left the house and jogged to the woods. Finding a convenient spot, he stripped off his clothes. His superhero costume was under them.

It felt glorious to be about to go into action! He plunged deeper into the woods, imagining how terrific he looked.

In a quarter of a mile he came to a creek and followed its many twists and turns. On all sides the woods were alive with the warble of birds and the sounds of other wildlife.

No poachers anywhere along the creek.

Undeterred, Butch knew of two large ponds. They were on private property. There was no house. It was said that the man who owned the ponds had stocked them with fish and came there now and again to enjoy his own little fishing preserve.

A four-foot heavy gauge high wire fence was no obstacle. Butch ignored a large sign that proclaimed: *Private Property Keep Out.*

The ponds were huge, one slightly elevated above the other. He made a circuit of the first and was puzzled. There were no traces of muskrat activity. No holes. None of the trails they made. Nothing. His puzzlement grew as he made his rounds of the next pond.

He went completely around and stood in the bright sunlight wondering where he should look next.

"What in God's name?"

Startled, Butch glanced up at the earthwork between the ponds. There, silhouetted against the sun, stood an elderly man with a fishing rod in one hand and a tackle box in the other. His eyes were wide and his mouth hung open.

But it wasn't the man that arrested Butch's attention. It was the two large Huskies, one on either side of the man, their heads cocked and their foreheads pinched as if they were as perplexed by what they beheld as their owner.

The man found his voice. "Who are you, boy? What are you doing here? And what on earth are you wearing?"

Butch's head filled with images of being turned over to the police and having his mom called and him being grounded without an allowance forever. He whirled and ran.

"Stop!" the man cried. "Come back here!"

Butch wasn't about to do any such thing. The fence wasn't more than fifty feet away.

"Ceasar! Brutus! After him! Sic him! Sic him!"

Butch looked back.

The Huskies barreled down the rise obedient to their master's wishes.

Butch flew. He knew he couldn't possibly outrun a pair of dogs. But if he could reach the fence, if he could get over it, he might be safe.

His stag-handled knives flapped wildly on his hips. The big knot on the top of his head was doing a lot of flapping of its own.

He vaulted a log and streaked around a boulder and

weaved through several trees and was almost there.

Another glance revealed that that Huskies were gaining.

"After him! After him!" the man shouted.

What was wrong with that guy? Butch wondered, and then there wasn't time for anything except grabbing hold of the fence and levering himself up in a frantic scramble. He heard a growl behind him and as he came to the top, there was a loud gnashing sound and something struck his right foot a glancing blow. Then he was over and sprawled to the ground as the Huskies lunged against the fence in a bid to reach him.

Heaving upright, Butch gained the cover of the forest. He could hear the dogs snarling and barking and the man shouting.

He came to where he had stripped off his clothes and hastily donned them. His mask, he stuffed into his underwear.

All the way home he listened for sounds of pursuit but there were none.

Once safe in his bedroom, Butch pulled the nylon mask out of his underwear and placed it on his bed and stared at it. This superhero business wasn't all it was cracked up to be.

Maybe it was best if he choose a different career. What, time would tell.

Life went on.

Right before the new school year, Butch's mom took them to a clothing store in Trooper, which she had been doing for several years now. They went in but before they could begin to shop, the owner took his mom aside and the pair talked in low tones for a while.

Butch could tell his mother was upset. Finally she ushered the three of them outside and took them over near an alley.

"I'm sorry," she said, her face etched in sorrow.

"For what, mom?" Karen asked.

"He won't let me buy you new clothes this year."

Butch didn't understand. "Why not?"

His mom sighed and gazed at the sky and then looked at each of them and mustered a wan smile. Her eyes filled with tears. "Because I haven't paid off last year's bill. He says unless I do, he won't sell me any new clothes." She stopped and bowed her head. "I just don't have the money, kids. You have no idea how hard it is to be a single mother raising three children by yourself. It's all I can do to keep food on the table."

"But you're a secretary," Karen said.

Their mom gave an odd little laugh. "Most secretaries don't make all that much, sweetie." She glanced toward the store. "I don't know what to do."

"We can keep wearing the ones we have," Butch said.

"They're kind of worn," his mom said. "And you've practically outgrown yours, you've shot up so fast. The bottom of your pants barely come to your ankles."

"I don't care," Butch said.

"Me either," Karen said. "Let's do like he says and wear the ones we have."

Mark smiled and nodded.

Butch's mom swallowed and her eyes glistened as she squatted and held out her arms. All three of them moved in close and she gave them a warm, lingering hug. "My special babies."

On the farm Butch continued to devote a lot of his time to killing everything he came across; groundhogs, squirrels, pigeons, snakes, bats.

The latter were a special challenge. During the day they would cling to the inside of the shutters on the farmhouse.

To kill them he used an old rusted corn cutter his aunt let him have. It was shaped much like a machete.

Butch's bat-slaying technique was to stand next to a shutter, quietly undo the latch that held it in place should a storm or high winds arise, and then, as quickly as he could, fling the shutter wide and swing at any bats clinging to the slats before they could take hasty wing. Often he would shear a wing and they would flop about on the ground until he finished them off.

He never told anyone what he did. His killing was done in secret. Not because he cared what others might think. It was just none of their business.

Then one day he killed a bat at the back of the farmouse and after he shut and latched the shutter and bent to pick up the bat so he could take it out in the field and fling it into high weeds, he turned and was taken aback to find Aunt Evelyn in her bonnet and long dress giving him a look of disapproval.

"Why did you do that?"

Butch held up the dead bat. "I like to."

"How long have you been killing them?"

"A while now."

Aunt Evelyn gazed at all the shutters on the three stories. "No," she said.

"You don't mind me killing groundogs and pigeons," Butch said.

"This is different," Aunt Evelyn said. "Groundhogs eat our crops. The pigeons are a nuisance." She bobbed her chin at the bat in his hand. "They do us a service. Leave them alone."

"They do?"

"You've seen them in the evening. They come out and dive and swoop after insects. Moths, beetles, mosquitoes and more. It's especially good that they eat the mosquitoes. So yes, the bats do us a service. Leave them be."

Butch stared at the bat and the blood dripping from its body. "I didn't know. I won't kill them again," he promised.

Aunt Evelyn started to turn but stopped. "I haven't said anything but I will now. You kill too much. Almost as if it's your favorite thing to do."

"It is," Butch admitted.

"Why?"

"I like it."

A look of great sadness came over her. "Becky has no idea what she has wrought."

"Wrought?" Butch said.

"Think about something for me."

"Sure."

"I mean it. This is serious."

Butch waited.

"Think about only killing things that need killing. Not just for the fun of it. Only when it's necessary. Do you understand?"

"Sure," Butch said, although truth to tell, he didn't. Killing was killing. There didn't have to be a reason. It was fun.

He went on having fun until the day he killed Romeo and Juliet.

EPIPHANIES

Adjacent to one of the ponds on Doc McClendon's property was a springhouse. Cool and inviting on a hot summer's day, to Butch it was a dark, mysterious place with a hidden recess behind the spring that he couldn't reach.

It was also home to a pair of bullfrogs. The biggest and grandest frogs Butch ever saw.

He dearly yearned to do them in as he had so many other things. But they were always alert, always vigilant. No matter how quietly he snuck up on the springhouse doorway---which didn't have a door---the moment he entered, the bullfrogs would leap into the rock-lined well and disappear.

Sometimes he could approach but stay well back and watch from hiding. The bullfrogs would do what frogs always did, jumping and swimming and croaking now and again.

He wondered if the pair were in love, like people fell in love. He wondered if they were as devoted to each other as husbands and wives sometimes were.

One day the unexpected happened.

Butch was making a circuit of the pond on his way to the bamboo forest when he drew up short in surprise.

Not thirty feet away, right there in the bright

141

daylight, was the male bullfrog.

Butch scanned the vicinity and spied the female close to the male, both just sitting there and staring out over the pond.

This was the first time he ever saw them outside the springhouse.

To make things sweeter, he had his BB gun, a lever-action *Daisy* rifle.

A tingle of excitement rippled through him. Ever so slowly he raised the BB gun to his shoulder. He had already cocked it so all he had to do was aim and shoot.

He centered the sights on the male's large eardrum but didn't squeeze the trigger. He needed to be closer. Otherwise he might miss. BB's had a tendency to curve the farther from the target.

Scarcely breathing, he edged his right foot forward a few inches. When the bullfrog didn't react, he inched the left. Bit by bit he narrowed the distance, from thirty feet to twenty-five to about twenty.

Incredibly, the bullfrogs still sat there. Why, he couldn't guess. In the springhouse they were always so quick.

Butch took deliberate aim and fired.

At the first shot the male leaped into the air and then bounded toward an overturned rowboat set on blocks of wood. The female followed suit.

The boat was so heavy that Butch could only lift one end a few inches.

Flattening on his belly, he peered underneath. It was so dark under there that it took him a while to distinguish their silhouettes. He shot both, repeatedly. At each shot they moved but didn't emerge.

Then he saw one dart out the other side. Scrambling up over the boat, he spied the male making for cover in high weeds. He shot and hit it and it veered.

An instant later the female broke into the open, moving after the male.

Butch spun and shot her, cocked and shot her again on the fly.

Both bounded toward the weeds.

Butch raced in pursuit, firing as as fast as he could work the *Daisy*. He shot and shot, first at one and then the other. He didn't miss once.

Finally the male sprawled and slid and was still. The female stopped and turned to the male just as Butch put another BB into her and she collapsed nearly touching her mate.

Butch laughed and stood over them, flushed with triumph. He replayed the scene in his mind and realized it had taken nine BB's to kill the male, seven to kill the female.

He was impressed at how doggedly they sought to live and how determined the female was at the end to reach the male. Out of respect for the fight they put up, he laid them side by side with their forelegs touching.

"Romeo and Juliet," he said aloud.

Grinning, he went to leave but had only gone a short way when he was brought up short by a thought the likes of which he never had before.

It startled him.

Taking a seat on a log, Butch set the *Daisy* in his lap and stared for the longest while at Romeo and Juliet and at the pond. At the butterflies flitting about. At the dragonflies. At the ripples made by the sunfish. And at the frogs again.

He remembered the many times he had enjoyed watching them cavort in the springhouse. How....a word came into his mind....vital, and, in a way, beautiful they were.

And now they were dead. Gone. No more.

Thanks to him.

Butch's sense of triumph faded. In its place was a certain sadness.

He got up and left, telling himself that there was no reason to be upset. Living things killed other living things all the time. For food. To defend themselves. To protect their young. Sometimes, as he had read in a news account of a wolf that killed a dozen or so sheep, apparently for the thrill of it.

And look at what happened to his dad.

Death was part of life.

Inevitable for all things.

So when he killed, he was merely doing what so many other creatures did.

And in a sense, imitating God.

God created everything, they told him in Sunday School and at the Methodist Bible School. God had set up the way life was. And part of life was that everything died.

Still, it troubled him, killing Romeo and Juliet. As if he had wiped a small beautiful part of life away.

He didn't let it interfere with his work as an exterminator, though.

Local farmers had hired him to rid their farms of pests. Recently he had been called on to exterminate a large flock of pigeons from a silo.

The pigeons left each morning shortly after sunrise and returned each evening along about sunset, to roost. Most settled on-high. The only way to reach them was to climb a dung-encrusted ladder.

The reek and the filth didn't appeal to him, especially with his nose. He preferred to slay them from down low.

Using a gun was out of the question. At the first shot the flock would take frantic wing.

Butch favored his bow. He had practiced with the 35-lb pull fiberglass his mom bought him until he seldom missed.

His technique was to slip into the silo before the flock returned in the evening and wait for them to settle down---then pick them off. Often, he was able to shoot three or four before the rest caught on that something was amiss and scattered.

On this particular day he crept into the silo through the outer door. Placing himself in deep shadow, he slid an arrow from his quiver and notched it to the string.

He breathed shallow against the stink.

Now all he had to do was wait.

A loud rustle of wings served as a harbinger of their return. The top of the silo was kept open, and a virtual cloud of birds descended and with much fluttering and cooing roosted for the night.

Feathers drifted down. Droppings fell, some on Butch's head and shoulders. He didn't move a muscle.

Without warning a pigeon suddenly swept down onto a rung of the ladder not four feet above his head.

It made the usual fuss and soon quieted.

Butch couldn't believe his luck. It would be an easy kill. The only hitch was that the pigeon was in the same deep shadow and he could hardly see it. He decided to wait a bit.

Pale light began to creep down the 90-foot silo from the opening at the top. The moon was rising. A full moon, no less.

Scores of pigeons were revealed.

Butch would have plenty of good shots.

Long minutes went by with the stench in his nose and soft coos the only sounds.

On high, the moon in all its celestial brilliance filled the opening, lending the illusion that the interior of the silo glowed.

The light would soon reach the pigeon right above him.

Butch slowly raised his bow. Just as slowly he pulled back the string until the fletching brushed his cheek. He sighted down the arrow and fixed the hunting tip on the darkling shape.

Another moment, and moonlight bathed the pigeon in a soft radiance. There it perched, as clear as could be. It had fallen asleep with its head turned and its beak nestled into its feathers, a typical posture. But now it unexpectedly raised its head and looked right at him, as if somehow it had sensed his presence.

Butch was set to release but hesitated.

There he stood, his bow bent, his arrow ready to deal lightning death.

But he didn't let the arrow fly.

His eyes met the pigeon's---and the strangest

sensation came over him.

The pigeon---perched so still and peaceful---the iridescent moonlight---the backdrop of the silo---all combined to fill him with a sense of profound beauty.

Yes, it was only a pigeon, and yet it was so much more. It was a fellow creature endowed with the most wonderful reality there was---being alive.

The insight shocked him.

For the first time ever it dawned on him that life wasn't about death. Life was about living.

Life was a treasure. To be taken only when there was a specific need. As Aunt Evelyn had said.

A Sunday School lesson flashed through his mind. From the book of *Ecclesiastes*. He liked it so much, he had memorized it: *To every thing there is a season, and a time to every purpose under the sun. A time to be born and a time to die. A time to plant and a time to pluck up that which is planted. A time to kill and a time to heal.*

A time to kill, Butch repeated in his head. Not to kill all the time.

He had gotten it wrong.

It wasn't that God, personally, killed everything and everyone. All life had its *time*. When that *time* was up, the life ended. How the life ended varied but it was as simple as that.

Butch lowered his bow. The pigeon was still staring down, still looking him in the eyes. It cooed softly, melodiously.

Butch let the string relax and quietly opened the door and slipped out.

He came to another decision.

No more killing animals for the fun of it.

He needed a new interest---and he had already found it.

In his reading he'd come across Herodotus and was rarely so excited about anything as he was about his new passions and their devotion to an aspect of life that promised to fire him with new enthusiasms.

Those new passions?

The Spartans.

And enlisting in the military.

A (POSSIBLY TEMPORARY) FINI

PLEASE NOTE

This autobiography is as real and true as old letters, official records, newspaper accounts, a family journal and memory decades later can render the events.

The cause of the briefly mentioned sickly bouts turned out to be a birth defect. When David was 17 he was rushed to the hospital suffering severe abdominal pain. The doctors attributed it to appendicitis and he was hurried into surgery under the assumption his appendix was about to burst.

On opening him up the surgeon found that his small intestine wasn't attached where it should be---it was wrapped around his large intestine.

As a result, what should have taken barely two hours became five and a half. The surgeon separated his intestines and then reattached the small intestine.

Afterward, the surgeon assured David that he could now live a normal life free from the sickly bouts and pain.

As it turned out that wasn't the case.

Made in the USA
Las Vegas, NV
09 February 2022